NONPROFESSIONALS IN
PSYCHIATRIC REHABILITATION

APPLETON PSYCHIATRY SERIES

edited by

THOMAS F. DWYER, M.D.
FRED H. FRANKEL, M.D.
MICHAEL T. McGUIRE, M.D.

Department of Psychiatry
Massachusetts General Hospital
Boston, Mass.

APPLETON-CENTURY-CROFTS
Division of Meredith Corporation
NEW YORK

NONPROFESSIONALS IN PSYCHIATRIC REHABILITATION

The Psychiatric Aide and the Schizophrenic Patient

ROBERT B. ELLSWORTH, PH.D.
Research Psychologist
Veterans Administration Hospital
Roseburg, Oregon

Adjunct Associate Professor
Department of Psychology
University of Oregon
Eugene, Oregon

introduction by Esther Lucile Brown, Ph.D.

6127–1

Library of Congress Card Number:

68–10849

PRINTED IN THE UNITED STATES OF AMERICA

M–28888

PREFACE

87731

Today, approximately 500,000 nonprofessionals work directly with hospitalized psychiatric patients, with adult and juvenile inmates of correctional institutions, and in community action and antipoverty programs.* Whether or not nonprofessionals *should* work with the marginally functioning client is no longer an appropriate question. How best to maximize their effectiveness is the important issue facing the professionally trained psychiatrist, clinical psychologist, social worker, and psychiatric nurse. The nonprofessional's impact on the behaviorally maladjusted patient is far greater than has been recognized, even in his traditional role of custodian or jailer. Emerging from that traditional role, the nonprofessional appears to be making his greatest contribution in his contacts with those very clients whom the professional has largely been unable to help. Working with the economically disadvantaged client, the chronically hospitalized patient, the incarcerated inmate, and the lower socioeconomic outpatient, the nonprofessional may succeed where we have failed. If this be so, then our first impulse to train him as a "junior professional" may very well hinder rather than enhance his effectiveness. Needing examination, then, is the commonly held assumption that the nonprofessional should be trained as a substitute for more desirable but unavailable professional personnel. Rather, the nonprofessional can well make a unique contribution of his own, a contribution that goes far beyond that of helping to solve the manpower shortages in mental health rehabilitation.

Enhancing the nonprofessional in his contribution to psychiatric rehabilitation is the subject of this book. The approach used was that of altering the nonprofessional's role functioning in the rehabilitation setting, rather than retraining him through classroom lectures on psychological theory, workshops in group psychotherapy, and other traditional approaches to training. The psychiatric aide's greatest impact was found to be with patients who had previously failed to respond to those approaches requiring professional training, such as psychotherapy, chemotherapy, and electric and insulin shock therapy. Not only did the chronically hospitalized schizophrenic reach a higher level of adjustment in the experimental aide program, but also he was found to have had a better treatment outcome both one year and six years after release than did his nonexperimental counterpart. It was observed that the aide's altered role functions cannot continue without some modification in the roles of other personnel. Consequently, this report also examines the interdependence of role functions among aides, nurses, activity therapists, and other professional staff. As such, it should be of interest to a wide range

*This estimate was derived from two sources: (1) Highlights from a survey of psychiatric aides. Public Health Service Publication, No. 1151, Washington, D.C., 1964. (2) Riesmann, Frank. Strategies and suggestions for training nonprofessionals. Community Mental Health Journal, Summer 1967, pp. 103–110.

of mental health personnel, including those educators and practitioners in the fields of nursing, psychiatry, activity therapy, psychology, social work, and corrections.

The experimental program began in March, 1959, after six months of planning, and continued until the autumn of 1961, after some 30 months of operation. Each of the experimental and nonexperimental project patients returning to the community during this time was evaluated carefully three months and 12 months after release. In August, 1967, six years after the experimental program ended, a final survey of the status and whereabouts of all project patients was completed.

At each stage of the project, various people helped to determine its direction, operation, and outcome. The author is especially indebted to Dr. Harold Stokes, Director of the Fort Meade Veterans Administration Hospital; Dr. Larry Christienson, Chief of Staff; Dr. Leonard Abramson, Chief of Psychology Service; and Miss Ruth Larson, Chief of Nursing Service. Without the support of these key people, the project could not have been started. The final survey on the status and whereabouts of all project patients was completed more than eight years later, with the kind assistance of Dr. George Kish and Mr. Clifford Cook, Psychology Service; and Mr. Don Hartford and Miss Pat Bachand, Social Work Service.

The author is grateful for the support of Dr. Alfred Poore, psychiatrist during the first phase of the project, and Dr. Harlan Hermann, psychiatrist during the second phase of the project. In addition, the activity therapists were instrumental in supporting the aide role changes, especially Mr. Leland Bowles, O.T.; Mr. William Plunkett, Recreation; and Mr. Bud Limbo, Outside Detail.

The psychiatric nurses in the program especially deserve tribute. Acting as an intermediary between the professional and nonprofessional staff, the psychiatric nurse translates professional treatment concepts into operational procedures. The nurses in the program were highly skilled in working with aides, for they had learned that working through others could be highly beneficial. Their influence was not always apparent, but the author came to learn that the most important role is often the least visible. As a catalyst for action, the psychiatric nurse determines whether a program fails or succeeds. The author is grateful to the following nurses for their part in the success of the program: Mrs. Dorothy Giedd, head nurse; Miss Sandra Jensen, first activity nurse; and Miss Dorothy Erickson, second activity nurse.

A special debt of gratitude is extended to Mr. Francis Crackenberger, Mr. George Hawley, Mr. John McDermott, Mr. Jim Shinost, Mr. Jim Chapman, and Mr. George Hackworth, who were among the many psychiatric aides whose initiative, creativity, and involvement contributed immeasurably to the project's success. The program could not have had the impact it did on the hospital patient without the dedication of these men. Special thanks is also extended to the many evening shift aides, both in the Experimental and Nonexperimental Buildings, who provided hundreds of patient behavioral adjustment ratings during the project.

Mrs. Margaret Barron, the secretary to the research office, was of invaluable assistance in the research phases of the project. In many ways, it was she who held the project together by coordinating the data collection and follow-up information, the basis of the program's evaluation. Her many reports on the team meetings, research meetings, and daily events during the project form the basis of much of the content of this report.

In the final reporting of the project, the research staff of the Roseburg Veterans Administration Hospital have been of invaluable assistance. The author wishes to thank Mrs. Beatrice Zimmerman who typed the drafts of the project report, Mrs. Leslie Foster who edited the final manuscript, and Dr. Barry Childers who suggested changes that added a great deal to the coherence and logic of this presentation. The psychology graduate students in my seminar, "Research in Milieu Therapy," also helped clarify many of the issues discussed in this book.

The author is grateful to the Research Service of the Veterans Administration,* without whose support the project could not have been undertaken; and to the Research Committees of the Fort Meade and Roseburg Veterans Administration Hospitals whose encouragement and interest were of invaluable assistance in all phases of the project.

*This study was supported in part by Veterans Administration Research (8200) Funds.

CONTENTS

Contents

PART THREE   Appendices

INTRODUCTION

Anyone who had occasion to visit large mental hospitals prior to World War II can scarcely have forgotten those many "continued treatment" wards where almost the only staff were attendants. Their duties included doing the ward work or supervising patients in doing it, and maintaining a quiet ward with the minimum of disturbance possible. Otherwise the attendants were likely to spend their time talking to each other, reading comic books, or trying to sustain their boredom until the end of the shift or duty. Few of them attempted to interest patients in games or in any activity other than ward work. As a result patients on many wards spent much of the day sitting listlessly looking into space, thus regressing farther both mentally and physically.

This was the pattern that prevailed in scores of mental hospitals (and still prevails in places) where, except for the relatively small active treatment service, the care of patients was viewed primarily as that of custody, not treatment. Although mental hospitals contain more than half of all the hospital beds of the United States, they were granted so little financial support, their prestige was so low, and their expectation of improvement among the chronically ill was so slight, that almost no psychiatrists or registered nurses could be recruited to staff the continued treatment areas. Hence these areas were like small isolated institutions within the larger institution, where inmates and attendants survived as best they could, and where the status of the latter, as viewed by the administration and the public, was only a little higher than that of the patients. It was indeed unfortunate, everyone agreed, that untrained persons had to be employed, but what else could be done! And since the attendants were untrained, how could they be of therapeutic importance to patients?

Fortunately, attitudes toward mental illness and the role of the attendant have changed markedly in the past quarter of a century. If they had not, the truly encouraging experiment that Robert B. Ellsworth reports in this book, would never have been undertaken. The use of corpsmen during World War II to nurse both physically and mentally ill service men demonstrated how effectively persons who had had short but intensive instruction could care for patients under the supervision of registered nurses. A young physician, who was detailed by the Navy to teach corpsmen, found the experience so gratifying and the implications for improved patient care so great, that later, as a resident in psychiatry, he started the experimental Menninger Psychiatric Aide School. Although some psychiatrists and psychiatric nurses thought the undertaking foolhardy, if not almost unethical, it accomplished much in its brief existence by focusing attention upon the greatly enlarged contribution of the attendant whose competence and status had been increased through a period of systematic preparation.

When the Veterans Administration reorganized its vast chain of hospitals after the war for the purpose of providing a medical service second to none in the United States, it was quick to see that the improvement of its neuropsychiatric hospitals would have to depend, to no small degree, upon recruiting and training a large corps of psychiatric aides. These aides would be expected to play a much more active role in social interaction with patients, the Veterans Administration maintained, than had generally been required. They were to be supported in this role not only through more adequate nursing and medical supervision, but through advancement in job grade and salary as recognition of gains in competence. The results, particularly in the more dynamic hospitals, were conspicuous indeed. They also helped appreciably to raise the sights of the state mental hospitals concerning what could be achieved through better selection and utilization of aides.

As a consequence of these and other trends, it became almost fashionable in the 1950's to speak of the aide as "the most important person" in reference to patients in mental hospitals. Although attitudes had certainly changed, there was reluctance to analyze the implications of the phrase in any way that was meaningful either to the professional persons who used it or to the aides themselves.

This reluctance was clearly demonstrated at a two-day conference of a small group of psychiatrists, nurses, and social workers, to which I had the good fortune to be invited, that had been called expressly to discuss the role of the psychiatric aide. In recognition of the importance of the aide, one of the psychiatrists had requested permission to invite three graduates of the Menninger Psychiatric Aide School. During the first two sessions not one of the three participated verbally in the informal discussions, and none of the professionally trained persons so much as asked them for an expression of opinion. Fortunately two of the discussants became aware of the fact that the group was only repeating the customary practice of unconsciously restricting communication and decision making to those persons whose professional training had conclusively led them to assume that they "know best."

With a somewhat painful effort this problem was raised for discussion at the third session. The response both from the professionally trained members and the aides, once the problem became clear, was immediate and profound. The psychiatrist chairman begged pardon for the sin of omission of which he and his colleagues had been guilty because of unawareness, but the implications of which they could see distinctly once it had been brought to their attention. The psychiatric aides, in turn, although trembling from inner tension, described how they had felt as they sat through hours of hearing their group talked about and planned for. It was as if that group were *things* to be used, never persons to be consulted concerning what they wanted, needed, or thought they could accomplish. The meeting proved to be a true group therapy session; probably everyone attending it can still recall the emotional release experienced as some of the status barriers to communication were lowered.

Within his description of the experimental project he designed for the purpose of increasing and then measuring the effectiveness of aides in one psychiatric hospital, Dr. Ellsworth notes the psychological difficulties encountered, because of a similar problem of perception, in permitting the aides a significant role. His explanation is particularly convincing because of his willingness to admit to the reader his own surprise in discovering how much he could learn about patient behavior once he tried to listen to what the aides were telling him in their incorrect and often crude English. He is even open enough to testify to his own reaction of psychological withdrawal when an aide first dared to disagree with him.

If a seemingly disproportionate amount of space has been devoted in this Introduction to the reluctance of professional persons to encourage the aide to play a larger role, it is for a specific reason. Recently it has become quite clear that increasing use must be made of many hundreds of thousands of persons without professional preparation, not only in mental hospitals and prisons that are also undergoing large if belated change, but in general hospitals, nursing homes, clinics of many kinds, social welfare agencies, public schools in deprived areas, and the new programs designed to improve the standard of living of the socially and economically disadvantaged. At no time in the foreseeable future will fully trained persons be available in adequate numbers for the tasks needed desperately to be done.

Even if such persons were available, there would probably still remain the difficulty of the social distance, resulting from differences in values, ways of living, and the use of language, that tends to separate the upper-middle class from the larger sectors of the population. Here is where representatives of those larger sectors have a distinctive advantage. It is generally easier for them to understand the motivations, needs, and behavior of, and to engage in helpful social interaction with, the members of groups appreciably like themselves than it is for persons who have undergone specialization into a profession. Recognition of this fact, therefore, is a first prerequisite in considering the nature and scope of the role that assistant personnel can be expected to fill.

No one should assume, however, that the mere provision of opportunity for aides to use their potential skill in social interaction, as well as those technical skills taught them in in-service programs, will guarantee achievement on the job. Much more is necessary. In *Nonprofessionals in Psychiatric*

Rehabilitation, Dr. Ellsworth has outlined another very important requirement that must also be met if the usefulness of assistant personnel is to be maximized. The aide must be furnished with a work situation that is conducive to his assuming a more active role, where both he and the patients know what is expected of them, where he can be assured of psychological support and guidance in the anxiety-inducing task of continued contact with the mentally ill, and where he can also be assured of reward for his efforts through being consulted about patient behavior and being included in the planning for patient care.

So basic are the psychological concepts underlying this requirement that they merit attention wherever assistant staff are employed. (The motivation and competence of many professional persons might also be improved were hierarchically structured institutions reexamined in the light of these same concepts.) It must be understood, however, that it is far from easy to create a work situation that adequately serves the psychological needs of staff and also of patients or clients. Institutional difficulties arise, even though the experimental plans have been well formulated and many of the potential pitfalls foreseen. Dr. Ellsworth describes how he attempted to establish a desirable work situation, and what modifications were subsequently made in his continuing efforts to improve it. That he succeeded to the extent that he did impressed me very favorably on the occasion of a brief visit to the project; the written report that he presents here makes interesting and instructive reading.

Various indications are offered of the satisfaction experienced by the psychiatric aides as their role became enlarged and more clearly defined, their expectation of patient improvement strengthened, their spontaneity in interaction with patients and professional staff increased, and their sense of importance raised through participation in the ward staff meetings. So far as the schizophrenic patients were concerned, the extensive statistical data presented show positive results not only in the number whose social adjustment in the hospital improved as compared with those on the nonexperimental wards, but also in the number who were rehabilitated sufficiently to return to the community. Interestingly, the more chronically ill patients, who have been the despair of mental hospitals, benefited from the program to a larger degree than did those who were more acutely ill. And now, six years after the completion of the project, a recent follow-up study shows that the proportion of such patients living outside the hospital has increased markedly.

The reader will probably conclude that this project has furnished further delineation of important guidelines that appear to have general applicability to the effective use of aides wherever and under whatever title they may be employed. Yet the report notes how few of the components of the experiment have survived the erosion of even the brief period of time since its completion, and how small has been its influence upon other units of the hospital. (Perhaps the most significant outcome has been the impetus it gave the institution to begin a trend of community placement.) Lest some persons, who may be uninformed about the current effects of social science research, conclude that either the research was inadequate or the hospital exceptionally traditional in outlook, I must reinforce Dr. Ellsworth's comment that such an outcome occurs frequently. Many encouraging experiments that I have had the opportunity to observe have disappeared so quickly after their official termination that interested persons who went to see the developments, upon reading about them in the published report, found scarcely any traces left.

The importance of applying to the practice of medicine what is learned from research in the physical and biological sciences has long been almost taken for granted. Although research in the behavioral sciences has made conspicuous gains in recent years, many administrators and other persons in positions of responsibility are not yet aware that it too may provide them with a significant instrumentality for improving aspects of patient care. If helpful knowledge obtained through experimentation, which is often long and costly, is not to continue to be lost to the participating institution, two steps need to be taken at once. One is an intensified attempt to learn *how* useful results, as well as positive attitudes toward the importance of behavioral research, can be built into the social structure of the institution. Thus the utlization of new knowledge would not have to depend so heavily as at present upon the sponsorship and support of one or two influential persons who might perhaps leave the particular institution at any time. The second step is the inclusion of enough social science content in the curricula of professional schools to guarantee that graduates have some broad understanding of the nature and potential significance of behavioral concepts and methods of investigation.

ESTHER LUCILE BROWN, Ph.D., Consultant
Psychosocial Aspects of Patient Care
San Francisco

November, 1967

NONPROFESSIONALS IN

PSYCHIATRIC REHABILITATION

PART ONE

Historical and Theoretical Background

1

Professionalism and Treatment Effectiveness in Mental Health

The past 25 years have witnessed a concerted effort to increase the public's concern about, and support of, the issues of mental health and illness. The newspaper crusades of the 1940's called attention to the deplorable conditions existing in many publicly supported mental hospitals of that time. Recent developments in treatment and rehabilitation of psychiatrically disabled people have done much to warrant increased public confidence in the mental health professions. Mental health care is now in demand. Patients seek admission to psychiatric hospitals. Community mental health centers have long waiting lists, and public mental health budgets are receiving more adequate support.

Despite the increased demand for mental health service, however, the public still does not understand clearly the means by which people receive help in the mental hospital or community clinic. A first-time visitor to the mental hospital, for example, finds himself entering a setting quite different from anything he has experienced before. It does not quite resemble a prison because people seem to walk about freely and there are no guards or high walls. On the other hand, one finds that some people are kept behind locked doors and senses that the patients are not quite free to leave at will. Nor does the mental hospital resemble the medical hospital in the visitor's own community, for mental hospital patients are not kept in bed but instead perform many of the functions expected of citizens in a small community. Some patients work in the laundry, some in the kitchen, and some help maintain the grounds. Although such activities are referred to as treatment, the visitor finds it difficult to conceive of them as such.

Having read that mental hospitals are critically short of staff, the visitor is puzzled to learn that there are often as many staff as patients. Upon further inquiry, he is told that only a few of the hospital's personnel, including college-educated people who have received additional training in the areas of activity therapy, nursing, social work, psychology, medicine, and psychiatry, are referred to as the treatment team or professional staff. What the differences are between these various professional groups is not always entirely clear, for the visitor observes all of these personnel talking to and doing things with patients. Also to be observed are a large number of other personnel who interact with patients; these are the attendants or psychiatric aides. Not having received college or professional training, these nonprofessional personnel nevertheless appear to be talking and doing things with patients in much the same way as do the professional staff.

Perhaps even more surprising is the discovery that the staff themselves are not entirely clear about what each of them should do, or can do best. Sometimes a patient's family find themselves talking with an aide or nurse who knows more about their hospitalized relative than does the ward doctor or social worker. The patient may also inform his family that his group therapist is a nurse rather than a psychologist, or that a psychiatric aide has helped him more than anyone else. At this point the stranger to the mental hospital begins to learn that much of psychiatric treatment is based on verbal and behavioral interaction with patients. And further, that interaction with patients is everyone's business, regardless of what his title may be and whether or not he has had professional training.

Although interaction is the foundation of patient rehabilitation and although all staff do interact with patients, the visitor to the mental hospital discovers the paradox that those who interact most with patients are regarded as the least important members of the hospital staff. If the visitor attends a staff meeting, he finds a clear-cut status hierarchy among staff, that is, the professional staff talk and are listened to more than are the nonprofessional psychiatric aides, the doctors more than the nurses, and so on. In these staff meetings those who have the greatest amount of patient contact (i.e., the aides and nurses), talk least about the patients.

Only recently have medical staff accepted other professional members as active participants in patient treatment and rehabilitation. A great deal of controversy occurred as each group sought membership and status in the treatment team. Those who had already achieved full status often opposed the recognition of the newer professional groups, or attempted to limit their function. Whether or not psychologists, social workers, and nurses should engage in counseling and psychotherapy is still debated to some extent, although few today would seriously question their assuming a legitimate role in mental health.

More recently, questions have arisen concerning the utilization of nonprofessionally trained personnel in mental health. The increased demand for mental health services, both in the mental hospital and in the community center, has resulted in a serious shortage of professionally trained manpower. Questions are now being asked with respect to new roles for nonprofessionals in mental health. Can the psychiatric aide, for example, contribute more than he has been to the rehabilitation of the hospitalized patient? Are there effective treatment techniques that can be taught to nonprofessionals? Despite the increased interest in utilizing nonprofessional manpower, however, there is a great deal of reluctance to move ahead rapidly in seeking answers to these questions. Blocking progress in this area is the long-held assumption that extensive professional training is the necessary foundation for treatment effectiveness. Even if this assumption should prove erroneous, the acceptance of the nonprofessional would still be opposed by many professionally trained personnel.

RECENT ATTEMPTS AND PROBLEMS IN INVOLVING NONPROFESSIONALS IN TREATMENT ROLES

The possibility of using nonprofessionally trained personnel to counsel emotionally disturbed people has only recently been explored in demonstration projects and research studies.* The National Institute of Mental Health supported a pilot study in training college-educated married women to become mental health counselors (Rioch et al., 1963). Despite the demonstrated effectiveness of this approach, Rioch (1966, p. 290) questions: "Why do they (the professionals) move so slowly if at all in using some of the new ways of alleviating the manpower shortage in the mental health field which have at the very least a good chance of success?" And further: "Why do we bring out all the regulations of academia and bureaucracy to make the hiring of people trained in nontraditional programs difficult, and the setting up of such programs frustrating?" (ibid., p. 291). A similar viewpoint was expressed by Sanders (1965) who found a great deal of verbally expressed interest in the training of nonprofessionals at the Philadelphia State Hospital, but few if any job opportunities for them, once they were trained.

Recently it was reported that long-term psychotherapy, designed

* A recent survey by Cutter and Zappella (1967) describes the increasing utilization of nonprofessionals in mental health counseling.

to help the client gain self-understanding, is not always necessary. Levy (1966) has outlined an approach, limited to only six sessions per client, that has proven extremely effective in preventing psychiatric hospitalization. Not only is this approach significant because it allows the professional to work with a larger number of clients, but it also appears simple enough to use in training nonprofessionals. Thus the approach of traditional psychotherapy, with its complex training requirements, may not be necessary or even desirable for helping certain groups of clients. The economically disadvantaged client, for example, is generally unable to accept or profit from traditional long-term psychotherapy (Yamamoto and Goin, 1966). In working with lower socioeconomic groups (Jacobsen, 1965), brief counseling that focuses on the immediate crisis appears to be a more effective approach than traditional psychotherapy.

Another approach to helping the economically disadvantaged with nonprofessional manpower is that outlined by Reiff and Riessman (1964). Neighborhood counseling centers were set up in areas where economically deprived people lived. They were staffed with people who had the same socioeconomic background as the clients they served, and who were felt to have a natural talent for counseling others. These investigators point out that it is the economically disadvantaged person who often desperately needs help but for whom help is not available in his own community. Once in the mental hospital, he rarely receives psychotherapy as does his middle-class counterpart, but is treated instead with electric shock and medication. By developing a community-based service in which the poor are helped by others of similar background, these investigators hope to offer one solution to a problem not yet solved by professionally trained staff.

Should some or even all of these different approaches prove effective, it is unlikely that most professionally trained personnel will find them easy to support, let alone help to develop them. Some will actively resist them as suggested by one nonprofessional's experience; "The first month (of the second semester) was marked by an upsetting encounter with a social worker, who spent a half hour demanding heatedly what business I thought I had doing this kind of work, and was I aware of all the damage I could do" (Donner, 1965, p. 10). In order to handle this kind of resistance effectively, an attempt must be made to understand its basis. To answer the question of "what business" nonprofessionals have in the mental health field, one must know something of the assumptions and values of professionalism. To determine whether or not "damage" is done by these personnel, the results of the few research studies in this area can be helpful. The next two sections of this chapter are concerned with these issues.

SOME ASSUMPTIONS AND VALUES OF THE PROFESSIONS

The growth of professionalism has been extremely rapid since the onset of the industrial revolution. In 1870 there were 86 professional people per 10,000 population, in 1950 there were 331 (Goode, 1957). The professional community has power over its members by selecting its trainees and setting standards for admission and expulsion. A common language, sometimes only partially understood by outsiders, is developed. Once in, few leave, and members of the same profession are bound by a sense of identity.

Professionalism in mental health is highly valued. Clinical psychology, social work, and nursing have all attempted to upgrade their status by raising educational standards, by seeking to obtain state licensing or certification, and by demanding the right to engage in traditional psychotherapy. Other mental health groups (occupational therapy, recreational therapy, and the like), while not aspiring to conduct psychotherapy, are seeking to raise their educational and training standards and thereby to increase their professional identity. In some states the psychiatric aide group is also beginning to introduce educational and training standards as a basis for advancement. Thus, almost every mental health group is in the process of obtaining increased professional status for itself.

Why is professionalism such an important goal? In part, it increases the status of its members and gives legitimacy to requests for higher salaries and other privileges. In part, it allows a group to have increasing control over its own activities and tends to free it from a subservient role in relationship to other professions. Also, full membership in a professional group implies a certain level of competence with respect to the performance of sanctioned activities. And finally, it establishes a sense of identity in that certain unique activities and role functions become, as it were, the "property" of that group.

Why do the established professional groups resist other related groups' attempts to attain professional status? Loss of the first advantage of increased professionalism, the right to higher salaries and other privileges, would not seem to fully explain this resistance. Losing control over a group's activities, the second advantage, may be objectionable to the well-established professions who may not want other groups to decide for themselves what they can do best and how they will do it.

The third advantage, the implication of competence that professionalism conveys, causes several problems in accepting others as full partners in patient rehabilitation. As Rioch (1966, p. 291) points out: "If we have invested long years of hard work in achieving a high professional status, including many courses that were dull and many examinations that were nerve wracking, and we are told that some young bit of a girl with no training can do the job as well as or better than we can, it is natural that we would try to find some objection."

Even though professionals realize that their professional training does not necessarily prepare them to do well the things that are part of their role functions, the mental health professions nevertheless continue to insist upon this preparation as a necessary prerequisite. This insistence is justified when a particular activity clearly requires a great amount of technical knowledge and skill (for example, surgery). How effectively one performs other activities, such as psychotherapy and counseling, may depend less on training than on other, more personal characteristics. Some untrained people are therapeutic, while some professionals are not, even though they are highly trained in the techniques of psychotherapy. A more complete discussion of this point will be found later in this chapter.

When the ingredients of one's effectiveness are unclear with respect to what personal characteristics (i.e., the ability to relate to people), versus what training requirements are necessary, the members of that profession need the protection of professional identity. When, on the other hand, it is clear to everyone who in his functioning is effective, who is not, and what training is necessary to produce competence, the need for professional identity is decreased. Consider the engineer. The public demands from the engineer what engineers themselves demand, and accordingly he does not need or seek the protection of his professional group (Goode, op. cit.). Much of the irrationality surrounding mental health groups' resistance to the professional development of others can be accounted for in these terms. Even when they realize that their professional training does not always adequately prepare them, they need the protection of professionalism and its implication of competence because standards of competence remain vague. Under these conditions, the protection that professionalism offers is highly valued and apt to be irrationally defended.

One final point in understanding this problem of resistance is that of identity. A group that has established a particular role function as its own (such as psychotherapy) is not likely to welcome sharing this role function with others, especially when the other group has little or no professional status (Ehrlich and Sabshin, 1964). "What do we have to offer that is unique?" is a question each mental health group asks itself. The problems of identity concern each of them. Considerable role blurring occurs in that many mental health groups find themselves doing similar things. Furthermore, there is no clear evidence to suggest that any one group does not do some things as well as another, even though their professional training may be quite different. This creates uncertainty with respect to the legitimacy of their own training. Because, under these conditions of uncertainty, professionalism is so highly valued, active opposition to further loss of "unique" function continues to exist.

THE RELATIONSHIP BETWEEN EFFECTIVENESS AND PROFESSIONALISM

What harm can a nonprofessionally trained person do when talking with a client about the client's problems? Over a hundred years ago, before professionalism had become much of an issue, the small moral treatment hospitals of this country were very effective in rehabilitating mental patients. Approximately 86 per cent of all admissions were released (Bockoven, 1956, p. 296, Table 7). Critically reviewing the treatment outcome of one of these hospitals (Worcester State), Dr. John Park found that 48 per cent of those discharged had never had a relapse 36 to 60 years following release (ibid., p. 295). Another 6 per cent had relapsed but were again discharged. Thirty per cent had relapsed and remained mentally ill. Sixteen per cent could not be located for follow-up. Compared with present-day return rates, these results are indeed surprising. Johnson and McNeal (1965), for example, report a return rate of 37 per cent within one year and 56 per cent within three years after release. Miller (1966) finds that 40 per cent of patients return within one year and approximately 75 per cent within five years of release. This remarkably effective approach of the 1840's, then, compares favorably with present-day release and return rates.

Without professionally trained staffs, as they are known today, what happened in the moral treatment hospital to account for these results? Bockoven summarizes his impressions: "Moral treatment might be defined as organized group living in which the integration and continuity of work, play and social activities produce a meaningful total life experience in which growth of individual capacity to enjoy life has maximum opportunity. The moral therapist acted toward his patients as though they were mentally well. He believed that kindness and forebearance were essential in dealing with them. He also believed in firmness and persistence in impressing on patients the idea that change to a more acceptable behavior was expected" (ibid., pp. 302–303). This suggests that the quality of staff-patient relationship rather than professional training has much to do with its therapeutic outcome.

Recently reviewing psychotherapy research, Bergin (1966) found that many untreated patients improve over time without formal psychotherapy. This so-called spontaneous remission can be explained, in many instances, with the nontreated control patient seeking and obtaining help from nonprofessionals (i.e., friends) and subprofessionals (i.e., clergy, teachers, and others). He also found clear evidence of a deterioration effect that occurs with some patients who are exposed to psychotherapy. This is offset by an improvement effect for other patients, and results in the typical finding of "no overall effect" for psychotherapy patients in general as compared with nontreated controls. Some research suggests that experienced therapists have somewhat better results than inexperienced ones, as do therapists who are not personally maladjusted. Several other studies, however, have shown that the successful therapist is one who is warm and genuine. Personal characteristics of the therapist appear more highly related to effectiveness than the type of training he has had. Bergin (ibid., pp. 241–242) states: "This also indicates that titles, degrees, or years of training should not define the psychotherapist, but rather what the individual can do."

Other studies have shown that the patients treated by nonprofessionally trained people improve more than do control patients. Chronic patients counseled by college volunteers have a much higher rate of release than expected (Beck, Kantor, and Gelinean, 1963). Patients seen by lay group counselors (Carkhuff and Truax, 1965) had uniformly positive and significant improvement over that of control patients. This improvement in ward adjustment occurred in spite of the fact that many of the raters were hostile to the idea that lay counselors were therapeutically involved with their patients.

In another recent study (Poser, 1966), chronic schizophrenic patients treated by both professionals and nonprofessional summer students showed significant improvement over that of control subjects. What makes this particular study especially interesting, however, is that patients in group therapy with summer students improved more than those treated by professionally trained personnel! Poser (ibid.) suggests that the students were more enthusiastic, flexible, and better able to try different approaches than their professional counterparts. He concludes (p. 289): "The present findings do, however, support the conclusions that traditional training in the mental health professions may be neither optional nor even necessary for the promotion of therapeutic behavior change in mental hospital patients."

Nontraditional approaches using professionally untrained personnel have been found to be more effective than traditional group therapy conducted by professionally trained therapists (Anker and Walsh, 1961). In this study, chronically hospitalized patients, who engaged in writing and producing a play, improved significantly more than their counterparts in psychotherapy. Nontraditional approaches with other groups as well (for example, behavior therapy), appear to offer a more consistently positive outcome than traditional psychotherapy (see Bergin's review, 1966). Research such as this has led to one conclusion that "All mental health professionals will be required to function in new ways. Currently defined areas of interest will be broadened and one may expect a re-definition of the particular prerogatives now assumed by psychiatrists, psychologists and social workers, nurses, etc." (Schulberg, 1966, p. 161).

This is not to say that progress with respect to involving nonprofessionally trained personnel and developing nontraditional programs will occur rapidly. Nor does it imply that some role functions do not require some kind of training. What is suggested, however, is that it is not clear at this point what functions require what type of training and what functions simply require the prerequisite of experience in living. In a real sense, few persons are "untrained" with respect to problems in living. Many, in fact, have acquired a wealth of experience in successfully resolving problems in their own lives. It is impossible to estimate just how many people obtain the help they need from such friends and relatives, and never require the services of a professional. Further research should clarify these issues and provide solutions that could help solve today's manpower shortages and result in greater benefits to clients.

The increased demand for mental health services, then, has raised several unanswered questions. Can the services that the public is now willing to make use of be provided? Are available services effective, or must better ways be found? Are methods now in use appropriate for all groups of people, the economically disadvantaged as well as the middle-class citizen? It has become increasingly clear that there is much that remains unanswered, and that new and more effective rehabilitation approaches must be found. Moreover, because of the serious shortage of professionally trained manpower, effective techniques that utilize the skills of nonprofessionally trained personnel must be developed.

THE BACKGROUND OF THE
FORT MEADE AIDE-ROLE PROJECT

Concerned with the issue of whether or not nonprofessionally trained manpower could be utilized effectively in psychiatric patient rehabilitation, the following question was raised: What would happen if a program could be developed in which the psychiatric aide *really* became an active participant in the treatment of the hospitalized schizophrenic? This question was of sufficient interest to the director, Dr. Harold A. Stokes, and the professional and nursing staff of the Veterans Administration Hospital, Fort Meade, South Dakota, so that plans were made to set up a demonstration program in which the focus of treatment would be the development of the psychiatric aide as the major rehabilitation agent. The director of the hospital believed that the typical psychiatric aide brought to his work a wealth of experience in problems of living. As a father and a husband and a person who shared much of the same background and many of the values of the hospitalized patient, the psychiatric aide represented a relatively untapped resource for participating effectively in the rehabilitation of the patient. These assumptions held by the hospital director and endorsed by the chief nurse, represented the ingredients necessary to ask the question, "What would happen if . . . ?"

My own background and experience at the Veterans Administration Hospital in Salt Lake City, Utah, had led me to become increasingly aware of the untapped potential of the psychiatric aide. During one study (Ellsworth, Bryant, and Butler, 1960) in which we observed the day-to-day interaction of the psychiatric aide and patient, I began to see that many of the behavioral changes that we observed in our patients arose out of this aide-patient interaction. In off-ward activities, for example, it was usually the aide who interacted with the patient during periods of disorganized and inappropriate behavior. It was also the aide who encouraged the reluctant patient to interact with others and the resistant patient to participate. These patterns of aide-patient interaction undoubtedly had much to do with changes in patients' behavior and subsequent improvement in their condition.

Increasingly, I found myself interested in creating the kind of program in which the psychiatric aide could become an even more active participant in interaction with, and decision making about, the patient. During 1958, I learned of an opening for a research psychologist at the Fort Meade Hospital. My contacts with the director and staff of that hospital convinced me that not only could a program be developed in which the aide played an active-participant role, but that the hospital would also meet the conditions necessary for systematic and controlled evaluation of such an approach.

During the late 1950's, questions were being raised by some regarding a fuller utilization of the psychiatric aide as a rehabilitation resource. Few if any, however, had translated these questions into an operational program. Aides were being encouraged to modify some aspects of their role and to engage in some activities such as conducting groups and interacting more with patients. What we wanted to do was to drastically modify the aides' role with respect to all phases of rehabilitation, including treatment and release planning. Furthermore, we were interested in evaluating such an approach as it affected not only patients' in-hospital behavioral changes, but as it related to release and post-hospital community adjustment. Other studies were then (and have since been) more narrowly conceived with respect to modifying the nonprofessionals' role and measuring treatment outcome. Nevertheless, there had been a beginning interest in this area. Since then, a body of knowledge has begun to emerge regarding the contribution that people without professional training can make in psychiatric rehabilitation.

The present study adds to the body of knowledge regarding whether or not the nonprofessional can make a significant contribution to rehabilitation. Conducting a study such as this in the mental hospital setting with male schizophrenic patients had both advantages and disadvantages. First of all, a good deal is known about the psychological nature of one of the major forms of mental illness, the schizophrenic disorder. A review of this information (see Chapter 2) offers several clues regarding the kinds of approaches most likely to be effective with these patients. Secondly, the nature of the ingredients that underlie effective treatment approaches are becoming better understood (see Chapter 3). And finally, a great deal is known about the psychiatric aide, his behavior, values, and resources (see Chapter 4). An understanding of these three areas should enable one to develop the kind of rehabilitation program that combines what is known about the nature of the disorder and why certain approaches are effective, with what is known about the aide and how best to develop his potential for therapeutic interaction.

The disadvantage of conducting this study in the mental hospital setting is that the concepts appropriate to using nonprofessional manpower in rehabilitating hospitalized male schizophrenic patients would have to be translated for application in other settings and with other groups. Whether the same principles will apply with nonhospitalized clients in mental health clinics and correctional settings, for example, will have to await further research. It is hoped, however, that what is learned in this study can provide guidelines for work in other settings. As outlined earlier in this chapter, many of the same problems exist in all rehabilitation settings: status hierarchies, defensiveness with respect to role function, resistance to role change and nontraditional programs, cherished beliefs regarding professional training and assumed competence, communication barriers between professionals and nonprofessionals, and the like. Our experience in dealing with many of these problems, then, should be of interest and value to anyone who has the opportunity to work with professionally untrained personnel. If this report accomplishes nothing else, it may lend support to the efforts of others who would identify with the advancement of knowledge and innovation rather than with the maintenance of professionalism and status quo in the area of mental health rehabilitation.

2

Concepts Underlying the Treatment of Schizophrenia

If one regards the schizophrenic reaction as a disease process, the treatment of choice is most likely to be one which focuses on the reduction of psychopathology. Those who hold such a viewpoint usually develop a treatment program in which the physical and somatic approaches are emphasized. If one regards the schizophrenic process as a psychological disorder, the psychotherapeutic approach is probably the treatment of choice. If, however, the schizophrenic disorder is regarded as a maladaptive behavioral reaction, then one is most likely to emphasize social rehabilitation programs in which the patient is helped to modify his behavioral response. In short, the assumptions one holds regarding the nature of the schizophrenic disorder itself will largely determine the kind of program that he is most likely to develop.

An examination of the language of the mental hospital reveals that the disease concept, to some degree at least, is an inherent part of all hospital programs. As in the medical hospital, the "patient" receives certain "treatments" which are "prescribed" for him in order to "recover" from his "illness"; and if he recovers it is hoped that he will not "relapse" and become "sick" again. Indeed, if one were to attempt to describe the present-day mental hospital situation in terms other than medical-organic-disease language, he would find it extremely difficult.

SOME CONSEQUENCES OF OVEREMPHASIZING DISEASE AND ILLNESS IN SCHIZOPHRENIA

During the first half of this century, the disease concept of mental illness was adopted. This overemphasis had some serious consequences for both staff and patients. The primary interest of the hospital staff

15

during this earlier period was to arrive at the correct diagnosis. This was usually accomplished after intensive examination and observation of the patient. Once the diagnosis had been established, such physical modalities as electroshock or insulin therapy were prescribed. If the patient did not respond to intensive treatment within a certain period of time, he was sent to one of the back wards. The hospital atmosphere was laden with pessimism since most psychotic patients had a guarded prognosis.

Ozarin (1954) has said of this period: "After visiting some thirty-five mental hospitals the writer has formed the strong conviction that much of the pathological behavior of the patients is a result of their hospital experience rather than a manifestation of their mental illness." What has been referred to as the self-fulfilling prophecy is thought by many to have resulted in large storehouses of hopelessly mentally ill. As long as the "hopeless chronic" patients were labelled and abandoned, few of them succeeded in being released. Most of them accepted their role as hopeless cases, and obliged by withdrawing and deteriorating in response to an environment of pessimism.

THE LABELLING PROCESS

The correctness of the disease concept of mental illness, or any other concept, for that matter, cannot be accepted or rejected with any confidence at this time. It makes a great deal of difference, however, if one engages in the labelling process that was so much a part of the disease concept of mental illness. The labelling process, even in most hospitals today, continues to exert its influence in many ways. Patients are labelled as assaultive, chronic, elopers, as the case may be, and are likely to maintain this identity long after their behavior has changed.

In the large institution, the staff have little opportunity to know their patients well. Consequently, it is much easier to deal with categories of patients, and the implicit assumption is made that patients possess traits that are static and resistant to change. Patient X is regarded as basically the same today as he was two years ago. The expectation is that he will be essentially the same two years from now. Order, routine, tradition, and similarity are stressed, while change and differences are largely ignored. A staff who anticipate little change, or have little time to react to differences in patients' day-to-day behavior, do not revise their labels. Under these circumstances, it is unlikely that labelled patients will change since the expectancies concerning their behavior do not change.

During the Fort Meade project, the consequences of the labelling process were repeatedly illustrated. In one staff meeting, for example, a patient hospitalized for several years was presented for discharge. The chief of service, who had known this patient, challenged our judgment in presenting him because the patient was, to him, "an old chronic" who was "withdrawn," "seclusive," "suspicious," and "sick." As he described the patient to us, it became hard for us to believe that he was talking about the same person we had come to know through our daily contacts. What was happening did not become clear to us until we realized that he was talking about Patient John-1957, while we were talking about Patient John-1959. To those who react to labels rather than people, the possibility of change is often completely disregarded.

There are many features of language itself that support the assumption that the world is a static nonchanging place. When we say, "John is smart," we imply that smartness is a relatively enduring characteristic of John. Johnson (1946, p. 124) states: "As it stands, the statement strongly indicates that John is always the same. Nothing is said about when, where, in what respects, or from what point of view, 'John is smart.'" When a patient is labelled as schizophrenic, the implication is that the patient *possesses* certain characteristics or traits that he holds in common with other schizophrenics. In fact, at one time in the recent past, if a dementia praecox patient recovered and left a hospital, it was assumed that the original diagnosis had been wrong. The patient was presumed to have a disease that was enduring and nonchanging.

Today it is more realistic to look at the patient as a *process*. At any particular moment, patient X, for example, appears to us to be doing certain things that are similar to what other persons with the same label are doing. Viewed in this way, patient X will not surprise us too much if he behaves differently tomorrow. It was interesting to note that our ward personnel, who knew their patients well, rarely used labels in talking about them. On the other hand, those relatively unfamiliar with a patient tended to use diagnostic and descriptive labels. Those who observe patients closely find that labels do not fit reality very well. A patient may be angry in response to the O.T. therapist, but the same patient may be friendly in response to a woman volunteer. He may cooperate in one activity, and may refuse to take part in another. A label implies the presence or absence of an attribute, *either* hostile *or* not hostile. The reality of the situation is that he is *both* hostile *and* friendly, in different situations, at different times.

Customary language, however, is basically inadequate to describe the person-as-a-process, reacting to, and affecting an everchanging situation. Not only is language inadequate in this respect, but the labelling process implies that man can be understood in simple terms. As one begins to know another person well, it becomes apparent that that person is indeed a complex social organism. As one begins to know each patient individually, *differences* become more apparent than *similarities*. Yet, the labelling process in general implies similarities rather than differences, an implication which neither fits the reality of the situation nor does justice to the complexity of the individual.

DISEASE CONCEPT CONVEYS AN EXPECTATION OF SICK BEHAVIOR AND PASSIVITY

A second consequence of overemphasizing the disease-entity concept is that ward personnel, directly or indirectly, may be encouraged to accept the sick behavior of the patient, to communicate to the patient that he is not responsible for what he does, and consequently to perpetuate his illness. This benevolent accept-the-patient-as-he-is approach is regarded by many as one which provides the necessary support to the patient who already feels inadequate and worthless. In reality, however, this approach reinforces these self-defeating attitudes on the part of the patient. If staff simply accept sick behavior, they communicate to the patient that "we expect nothing better of you." By communicating to the patient that his sick behavior is acceptable, the staff runs the very real risk of perpetuating the patient's pathology.

If, on the other hand, the staff are encouraged to approach the patient as if he were potentially capable of normal social interaction, this brings into play "... a whole network of expectations which often bring the patient into closer conformity with socially acceptable conduct" (Cumming, J. and Cumming, Elaine, 1957, p. 69). Rather than accept or ignore sick behavior, some authors have suggested that staff intrude upon and disrupt such behavior in a direct and confronting way (Appleby, L., 1958; Forrer, G. R., 1958).

A third consequence of overemphasizing the disease concept of schizophrenia is that the patient is likely to be regarded as a passive object to be treated, rather than an active participant in his illness and recovery. Polonsky, White, and Miller (1957) have suggested that dependency and regression in patients' adjustment are more likely to occur when staff regard the patient as a passive recipient, and that regression can largely be prevented if the patient is treated more as an active participant in his rehabilitation. Frank (1961) has documented in his own review of research literature that people who participate actively in problem solving show more attitude change than those who do not. The introduction of such programs as patient government and group-centered problem solving (Fairweather, 1964) is illustrative of programs that encourage patients to take an active role in managing their own lives and working on their own problems while in the hospital. Such programs contrast sharply with those based on the assumption that patients "possess" an illness best cured by outside agents such as EST, insulin, lobotomy, and medication.

Earlier research (Dobson and Ellsworth, 1960; and Ellsworth and Stokes, 1963) has shown that the staff of a high-turnover, short-term treatment hospital were more likely to regard the patient as an active participant than were the staff of a low-turnover hospital. The staff of the low-turnover hospital were much more likely to feel that patients get better because of medication, EST, and lobotomy. Furthermore, it was found that the staff of the low-turnover hospital felt that the patient became ill because of factors outside his control (physical deficiency, or unjust treatment from others) and that patients were most likely to leave the hospital when their relatives wanted them back home. The staff of the high-turnover hospital, on the other hand, felt that the patient became sick because he was unable to handle the problems of living, got better because the hospital provided a nonstressful situation in which he could recover, and left because he worked for it. Between 1959 and 1962, the low-turnover hospital increased the turnover rate for chronically hospitalized schizophrenics and decreased the length of stay for schizophrenic admissions. During this period it was found that the staff increasingly perceived the patient as an active participant in his illness and recovery (Ellsworth and Stokes, 1963).

THE ADVANTAGES OF THE
BEHAVIOR MODIFICATION APPROACH

In our development of the aide-interaction program, we de-emphasized the physical treatment and traditional psychotherapy approaches. Our position was that we did not know what caused schizophrenia, but that we did know how to increase the probability of a rapid recovery: namely, through direct, open, and confronting interaction with the patient. Both the physical and psychotherapy approaches require skills developed through professional training and, had we emphasized these approaches, we would have communicated to the aide that he was a poorly prepared member of the treatment team. We were interested in adopting a framework in which the aide could play the active role in helping patients. For this, the behavior-modification approach seemed most appropriate.

To one who emphasizes physical treatment or psychotherapy, an approach of modifying the behavior of the patient is likely to be regarded as superficial. Myerson himself (1939), who introduced the total-push concept, did not feel that total push was a cure for schizophrenia, but only a method of improving the patient's behavior. Others regard the more recent resocialization techniques as approaches which modify the accessory symptoms of schizophrenia, but not the basic pathology itself (Appleby, 1958; Pace, 1957; and Forrer, 1958). Others disagree (Paunez, 1954; Unterberger, 1959; Sanders et al., 1961; and Fairweather, 1964), and regard social deficit as a primary disability for many schizophrenics. Boyd et al. (1954) and Kellam (1961) report that as the schizophrenic patient begins to interact with others, symptoms such as delusions and hallucinations begin to disappear.

In our own previous work (Ellsworth and Clayton, 1959) a highly significant relationship was found between the amount of staff-rated psychopathology and the level of aide-rated behavior adjustment. Furthermore, patients who showed an increase in behavioral adjustment tended to show a proportional decrease in psychopathology. Thus, a basic similarity is found in evaluating patient adjustment and improvement from either the behavioral or psychopathological point of view.

There are differences, however, for some patients who show a minimum of psychopathology are not necessarily well adjusted from a behavioral standpoint. Adjustment, as viewed from the psychopathology standpoint, is traditionally judged as an *absence* of symptoms. Two patients, both of whom show little or no pathology (hallucinations, apathy, delusions, and so on) are often very different with respect to their skill in interpersonal and problem-solving behavior. Some relatively "sick" patients are able to leave the hospital, find and keep a job, and maintain themselves in the outside world. Many patients who show a minimum of psychopathology are not able to do so (Ellsworth et al., 1958).

Several rehabilitation programs for the chronically hospitalized schizophrenic patient have used the behavior modification approach with significant results. Galioni et al. (1953) were able to discharge 19 per cent of 200 chronic patients involved in an 18-month experimental rehabilitation program designed to increase their level of social functioning. At the same time, only 5 per cent of the 200 matched control patients were able to achieve a release. These experimental patients were not simply discharged, unimproved, into the community, but had improved significantly in their behavioral adjustment as a result of the program.

The discovery that a patient's psychiatric status improved when exposed to a program focusing on behavioral adjustment has been reported by others (Appleby, 1963; Bartemeier, 1956; Boyd et al., 1954; Cameron et al., 1955; Cumming et al., 1956; Forrer, 1958; Freeman et al., 1958). The probability of release also increases following this improvement (Miller and Clancy, 1952; Miller, 1954; Sanders et al., 1961; and Unterberger, 1959). In our own work with chronically hospitalized schizophrenics (Ellsworth et al., 1958) it was found that 54 per cent of 72 chronically hospitalized patients were able to leave the hospital within a four-year period. The adjustment level, as measured by the Hospital Adjustment Scale (Ferguson et al., 1953), showed that these patients had gained about 23 percentile points in behavioral adjustment prior to discharge. Thus, when social behavior modification programs are used not only can the behavior of chronically hospitalized patients be significantly improved, but the probability of release is enhanced.

Not only are many of these behaviorally oriented programs measurably effective, but the use of a behavioral-adjustment approach largely avoids the potential dangers of the disease-entity concepts outlined earlier. Further, these kinds of programs, rather than perpetuating the illness by focusing on the pathology of a patient, hold the patient accountable for his behavior. And finally, the behavioral approach represents a framework that is more readily understood by all staff, as contrasted with the framework of psychopathology that requires the expertise of the professional.

A THEORY OF SCHIZOPHRENIA COMPATIBLE WITH THE BEHAVIOR MODIFICATION APPROACH

Documenting one best theory to explain the schizophrenic process, or one best treatment in helping him recover, seems remote at this time. When one reads the description of one theorist's analysis of the schizophrenic disorder, he thinks to himself, "Yes, I know patients just like this who seem to have this very difficulty . . . but I also know others who don't." Some schizophrenic patients are frightened, withdrawn, inadequate people who seem to fit so well the social-deficit concept of schizophrenia. Some are confused and disorganized, and illustrate the concepts of psychopathology. Others function on a well-integrated level in the hospital, but tend to break down when they re-enter the community. Still others, particularly newly admitted patients, appear very anxious and distressed and seem to feel the hospital is a temporary refuge in which they can regain confidence, perspective, and self-esteem. These various reactions are often labelled schizophrenic, but this does not help one to understand them.

A common distinction is that of chronic and acute. The acute schizophrenic is often a person who has effective social skills and who is able to empathize and relate to others as well as most normals. The chronic patient tends to react differently in his response to others and in his ability to empathize, role play, and so on. A similar distinction is that known as process and reactive schizophrenia. There appears to be a good deal of both clinical and experimental evidence to support the validity of such a classification (Becker, 1959; Bryant, 1961; Garmezy and Rodnick, 1959; Kantor and Winder, 1959; Phillips, 1953; and Zinet and Fine, 1959).

In general, the process schizophrenic has a premorbid history of social inadequacy, and rarely marries or relates to people effectively. He is likely to remain either chronically hospitalized or marginally adjusted in the community. The reactive schizophrenic has a good premorbid history and the onset of his illness is sudden rather than gradual. The prognosis of recovery for the reactive schizophrenic is excellent regardless of which form of treatment he receives.

Beginning with the writings of Federn (1952), a new viewpoint regarding the schizophrenic disorder has emerged. In reviewing this concept, the reader is referred particularly to the writings of Federn (ibid.), Szasz (1957), Freeman et al. (1958), and Des Lauriers (1963), who postulate that the central feature of the schizophrenic process is a disturbance of the development and maintenance of adequate ego boundaries.

The ego boundary is the edge of experiencing "self" in relation to the outside world, the place where "I" leaves off and the outside world begins. The healthy individual is able to sense clearly what occurs inside himself and what lies outside himself. In early infancy, there is no distinction between the self (ego) and not-self. In the beginning, the child experiences both internal and external sensations as a continuum. Gradually, however, he learns to differentiate between the self and the outer world. It is at this point that the ego boundary begins to emerge.

With the schizophrenic, the first sign of ego-boundary breakdown, the boundary between self and not-self, is a feeling of estrangement.

The schizophrenic begins to lose his ability to relate to reality because he does not experience himself as real; i.e., as separated, bounded, and differentiated. His thoughts may become voices talking to him. He may identify his own feelings about himself as those he thinks others have toward him. Words are no longer symbols but concrete reality. This experiencing of the internal and external sensations as a continuum, regarded as the fundamental disturbance in schizophrenia, becomes the basis for such symptoms as delusions, hallucinations, and concreteness, typically observed in the schizophrenic patients.

Under experimental sensory deprivation, normal persons also experience a blurring of the distinction between "self" and the outer world. This blurring, when experimentally produced, appears to give rise to many of the symptoms observed in the schizophrenic reaction, suggesting that the breakdown of ego boundaries may indeed be one of the processes underlying the schizophrenic reaction. To quote Freeman et al. (1958, p. 51): "It is this factor of ego feeling or the ability to differentiate the self from the environment, that we regard as being damaged in chronic schizophrenia, thus leading to the patient experiencing internal and external sensations as a continuum. We believe that once this basic disturbance is appreciated, all other schizophrenic manifestations can be reviewed as necessary elaborations of it."

From this viewpoint, it becomes possible to understand why the hospital setting often enhances the illness of the patient, leading to his further deterioration rather than to his recovery. Hospitals in which patients sit idly throughout the day force the patient to focus on himself. Instead of providing a situation that brings the patient into contact with the external world, such hospitals encourage the progressive loss of the patient's ability to distinguish his own internal world from the world about him. The patient is often not quite sure how he got in the hospital, nor does anyone seem to be able to show him the way out. When he does something, he may find that no one responds to him. On other occasions, the same behavior may result in unwelcome hostility directed at him. Under these circumstances, one avenue of safety lies in retreating into one's own world of thoughts and sensations.

If the patient is roused to respond again to external stimuli, the boundary between self and other can be re-established. Such stimulation may take the form of psychotherapy, card playing, talking to an aide, or any other activity that brings the patient into contact with the world outside himself. In a sense, he is forced to attend to something that comes not from his own internal world, but from "out there." Over a period of time, as he begins to respond to, and to become aware of, the difference between external and internal stimuli, he loses the symptoms thought to be associated with disrupted ego boundaries. This would appear to be the most logical explanation of why, as the patient increases his interaction with others, the psychotic symptoms begin to disappear.

THERAPEUTIC INTERACTION WITH THE SCHIZOPHRENIC PATIENT

If one makes the assumption that many of the symptoms of the schizophrenic patient can be understood as a disruption of the boundary between the self and the environment, then treatment of the schizophrenic reaction can be viewed somewhat differently. Basically, an attempt should be made to help the schizophrenic become aware of the distinction between self and not-self. For example, Des Lauriers (1963) has developed techniques to help the patient identify as his own his experiences, sensations, and feelings. The therapist calls attention to what the patient is doing, commenting on his bodily posture, his gestures, his facial expressions, and the therapist's own reaction to him. In this way, the patient is helped to again identify and experience himself as real and separate from his environment. Recent treatment of chronic schizophrenics, based on this approach, has reported considerable success (Paige et al., 1964). In a sense, the therapist intrudes into the disorganized world of the patient and becomes an external stimulus that helps the patient re-establish his ego boundaries.

Szasz (1957) and Freeman et al. (1958) discuss the characteristics of the therapist which they regard as important in helping him interact effectively with his patient. Szasz, in particular, believes that the etiology of schizophrenia arises from the lack of persons extending themselves to the patient during his childhood. They would thus be unavailable for incorporation (i.e., the child was unable to make them part of himself). Because these persons associated with the child were often cold, aloof, and emotionally unavailable for incorporation, Szasz (ibid., p. 427) suggests that schizophrenia represents a deficiency of stored internal objects necessary for adequate ego function. Thus handicapped, the patient is poorly prepared to handle the stress of adolescence and early adulthood.

Both Szasz, and Freeman et al. postulate that the therapeutic personality is one who is able to establish a genuine relatedness with his patient. The successful therapist is seen as a "real" person who extends himself to the patient in a warm, spontaneous, open, honest way. A cold, distant, aloof person who is not emotionally available to the schizophrenic is thought to hinder the recovery of the patient rather than to help.

For yet another reason the openness, honesty, and realness of the therapeutic person may represent an important ingredient of therapeutic interaction with the schizophrenic. Bateson (1958) has identified a type of "double-bind" interaction that he regards as basic in the etiology and development of the schizophrenic disorder. In this type of interaction, the parents' words communicate one thing, but their actions convey a conflicting message. The therapist who remains aloof and keeps his real feelings from the patient may be perpetuating the double-bind relationship and the schizophrenic process itself. Other research (Mainord et al., 1965) has shown that the strategy of confrontation produces a better therapeutic outcome than one of diversion and impersonal generality as used in group therapy with chronic schizophrenic patients.

The research of Whitehorn and Betz (1954, 1957, and 1960) tends to document this viewpoint. With much the same training (ibid., 1954) some psychiatric residents had improvement rates (discharge and socialization) of 68 to 100 per cent with their schizophrenic patients, while others had improvement rates in less than one third of their patients. In a study of the successful and nonsuccessful therapists, they concluded that improvement was associated ". . . with the tactical pattern which has been characterized as 'active personal participation.' Inclusion in this category means that the record shows that the physician, in his transactions with his schizophrenic patients, manifested initiative in sympathetic inquiry, expressed honest disagreement at times, sometimes challenged the patient's self-deprecatory attitudes, set realistic limits to what he could accept . . ." (ibid., 1954, p. 330). Physicians who were either passively permissive or who interpreted and instructed, were those who failed to help their patients.

Whitehorn and Betz later confirmed these conclusions in a second and third study, using different approaches to an analysis of the therapeutic person (ibid., 1957 and 1960). In an independent study of the personal qualities of therapists with schizophrenic patients, Knupfer et al. (1959) found that effective therapists (supervisor's judgments) rated themselves as able to convey their feelings, including hostility and cynicism, while less effective therapists were more conciliatory and appeasing. A recent review of this issue (Carson, 1967), suggests that the therapist characterized by genuineness and openness is more likely to be effective in working with the distrustful-extrapunitive (acting out) patient rather than the trusting-intrapunitive patient. Since most of the schizophrenic reactions would fall in the distrustful-extrapunitive group, Carson's review lends support to the conclusion that openness and genuineness are important therapist qualities for working effectively with schizophrenic patients.

Rogers (1962) summarizes this viewpoint especially well. In discussing treatment of the hospitalized schizophrenic, he writes, "I want now to turn to learnings which are more personal, which have affected us more deeply as individual therapists. Perhaps the deepest of these learnings is a confirmation of, and an extension of, the concept that therapy has to do with the *relationship,* and has relatively little to do with techniques or with theory and ideology. In this respect I believe my views have become more, rather than less, extreme. I believe it is the *realness* of the therapist in the relationship which is the most important element. It is when the therapist is natural and spontaneous that he seems to be most effective. . . . Our experience has deeply reinforced and extended my own view that the person who is able *openly* to be himself at that moment, as he is at the deepest levels he is able to be, is the effective therapist. Perhaps nothing else is of any importance." (*ibid.,* p. 10).

One of the basic assumptions in the present book is that the psychiatric aide, in his interaction with the schizophrenic patient, can exhibit all of the characteristics of successful therapeutic interaction. In their observations of the psychiatric aide, Hyde *et al.* (1960) report that these personnel, generally less well educated than other psychiatric workers, are least complicated in their feelings toward the patient. The possibility that persons, not professionally trained in the techniques of psychotherapy, can play a significant therapeutic role has been difficult for many mental health professionals to accept. As indicated, the report of the very effective moral treatment hospitals of the 1840's (Bockoven, 1956) suggests clearly that the psychiatric hospitals of that era were highly therapeutic, despite the fact that techniques of formal psychotherapy, drugs, and other physical modalities were not known. In reading Bockoven's account of these small effective hospitals, one finds the quality of genuine relatedness clearly evident in the interaction of the patient and staff.

The staff of these moral treatment hospitals also believed that the patient was capable of normal behavior. By approaching the patient as if he were normal, they often found that the patient lived up to these expectations. This attitude is probably another essential ingredient of therapeutic interaction, and has been identified as characterizing the interaction of the psychiatric aide and patient. As Dunham and Weinberg (1960, p. 253) have found, the aide is more likely than other staff members to respond to the patient as if he were normal, and to treat him within this framework.

One problem, as Hyde and Williams (1957) point out, is that many psychiatric training programs have the effect of taking away from the aide the native spontaniety and freshness of human responses that are the ingredients of a therapeutic relationship and of giving in return only a shopworn bag of tricks. The adult aide often comes to the hospital already experienced in responding to others in a natural and untutored fashion. By training him to assume a role that is unreal for him, he is being, in part, robbed of his already established skills in interacting with other human beings. If one of the essential ingredients of a therapeutic relationship is indeed the ability to extend one's self to the patient as a real person, the psychiatric aide needs perhaps to have these qualities developed and enhanced, but he does not need to be re-educated.

SUMMARY

In this chapter I have suggested that the type of language used by mental hospital personnel in describing the patient conveys the assumption that mental illness is basically a disease entity. The earlier emphasis on diagnosing this assumed disease entity led the staff of the mental hospital to regard the schizophrenic disorder as a permanent condition that had little chance of remission. This earlier low expectancy for recovery was essentially self-fulfilling, since most of the patients hospitalized during the first half of this century did indeed become chronically institutionalized.

Even today, many personnel continue to engage in the labelling process and thereby create an expectancy for enduring behavior. Anticipating little change in labelled patients, these hospital personnel help perpetuate the behaviors associated with assaultiveness, chronicity, incompetency, and the like. The labelling process also implies that these enduring characteristics are an inherent part of the patient himself, and that the patient is not in the process of adaptation to an ever changing situation.

The labelling process and the disease-entity assumptions also imply that the patient is not accountable for his behavior, and that sick behavior is to be expected and accepted. Instead of an active participant in his own recovery, the patient is regarded as a passive object who is the recipient of treatment from others.

The behavior-modification approach, in contrast, assumes that patients react to the situation about them and that change is the rule rather than the exception. As a patient changes in his behavioral adjustment, such symptoms as hallucinations, delusions, and withdrawal decrease significantly or disappear entirely. Rehabilitation programs based on the behavioral-modification approach not only utilize the skills of nonprofessionally trained personnel, but also are effective in returning many chronically hospitalized patients to successful community living.

The ego-boundary theory of schizophrenia suggests that the behavioral-modification approach is not superficial, but represents instead a direct attack on the basic deficit underlying the schizophrenic process. Intrusion, confrontation, and interaction with the patient help him to again distinguish his internal world from the world about him. Gaining skill in re-establishing the boundary between "self" and "other," the patient begins to decrease his hallucinatory and delusional behavior. He is again able to identify his thoughts and feelings as his own rather than as coming from "out there."

Therapeutic interaction with the schizophrenic patient has been found to have the qualities of directness and openness. The successful therapist extends himself to the patient as a real person who is able to "be himself." It was proposed that if this is the essential quality of therapeutic interaction, the psychiatric aide, unencumbered by complicated professional training, is in an excellent position to help the patient. He is also more apt to react to the patient as if the patient were normal, and to become spontaneous, direct, and open in his approach to patients.

3

A Sociopsychological Interpretation of Traditional Treatment Approaches

If mental illness is regarded as a disease, the approach to treatment is one of finding a specific treatment agent that will affect the disease process. The history of psychiatric hospitals has been filled with the introduction of specific treatment approaches, each one regarded by its particular advocate as the ultimate in the treatment of mental illness. In 1937, Sakel announced that insulin treatment resulted in the full recovery of 70 per cent of schizophrenic patients. Theories were proposed to describe the effect of insulin on the metabolic function of the central nervous system. Some two decades later, Ackner et al. (1957 and 1962) found that the therapeutic response obtained through insulin treatment was related to the procedure itself, and was not a function of the specific chemical agent. In a very carefully controlled study, a group of schizophrenic patients who had been rendered unconscious by barbiturates, then brought back from an unconscious state, interacted with the treatment staff, and given the same number of treatments and the same type of hospital care as the insulin-treated group, recovered as completely from their illness as those who were given insulin. These authors believe that the therapeutic gains in insulin therapy arise from a group-influenced expectation for recovery and an increased contact with medical and nursing personnel. The effectiveness of this once popular organic treatment approach appears to be explained by this communicated expectation for recovery, the patient's belief that he is getting an effective type of treatment, and his interaction with staff who expect and support changes in him.

EST, once used with almost all schizophrenically diagnosed patients was found, through careful review of controlled studies, to have very little overall effect on the outcome of the disorder (Staudt and Zubin, 1957). Follow-up studies of lobotomy suggest that factors other than the operation alone determined the final outcome of the treatment ap-

29

proach (Witton and Ellsworth, 1962), although patients who underwent this form of treatment reported less anxiety and obsessive rumination following the operation.

One explanation for the reported early success of any new treatment approach is that the originator of the technique was biased, and that he exaggerated his reports of success. Another possibility is that he did indeed obtain the success rates he claimed. If one analyzes Sakel's reports (1937) carefully, one finds that many of the patients were taken from wards where they had little else to do but sit in relative isolation and boredom. From this situation, they were brought to a small well-staffed unit where people talked to and worked with them. They found that their doctor was optimistic and hopeful, and that his staff were not only genuinely interested in them, but fully expected that they would improve. The entire social climate of the treatment unit itself was conducive to change. As such, it becomes impossible to ascribe the patient's improvement to the physiological effects of insulin *alone*. To make the problem of insulin evaluation even more difficult, when a normally distant, aloof physician administers insulin, he behaves much more like his therapeutic counterpart by becoming actively and personally involved with his patients (Whitehorn and Betz, 1957). Thus, for him, insulin is the vehicle that helps him establish the kind of relationship most helpful to the schizophrenic patient. With the help of insulin, then, the hitherto aloof physician achieves the same results as physicians who were able to establish a therapeutic relationship without it.

I think that the effectiveness of any specific treatment approach will be determined largely by the extent to which it brings about a change in the expectation for improvement on the part of both patients and staff. A patient who receives EST or insulin is more likely to improve if the staff succeed in communicating to him their belief that he will get better. A patient, on the other hand, who is treated in a setting where the staff do not believe that a particular treatment approach is effective will be most likely to respond to this expectation by remaining largely unimproved. Viewed in this way, it is not at all surprising that the innovators of treatment approaches, not only enthusiastic themselves but also able to communicate their enthusiasm, usually obtain better treatment results than those who follow them. When a particular treatment approach is examined by skeptical investigators in a carefully controlled study, the specific treatment variable is found to have much less impact than was originally reported. Even if the treatment variable brings about measurable improvement, the effect of that treatment on the overall rehabilitation of the patient is likely to remain insignificant unless it sets off a cycle of: (1) staff expectation of, and reaction to, change,

(2) patient response to staff expectation and reaction to change, (3) further staff response to patient reaction, and so on. If this cycle is short-circuited by either patient or staff, it is likely that the patient will remain only minimally improved.

CHEMOTHERAPY

When one considers the enthusiasm for ataractic drugs in the treatment of schizophrenia, one senses this interaction between the effects of drugs, the resultant change in staff expectation, and their combined impact on further patient change.

For some hospitals, the tranquilizing drugs marked a turning point in their treatment effectiveness. The total population in New York's mental hospitals decreased over 1,000 per year after these drugs were first used (Brill and Patton, 1959). In 1959, approximately 55 per cent of all admission had achieved a release within six months, while in 1955, only 44 per cent had done so (Brill and Patton, 1961, Fig. 2). The proportion of patients who stayed on to become chronically hospitalized also decreased, with about 22 per cent fewer patients remaining beyond their fourth year of hospitalization (ibid., p. 6). In spite of the fact that readmissions increased almost 50 per cent (ibid., p. 3), there is no doubt the overall results were striking. Instead of the 105,000 patients they were expecting in 1961, they found instead only 89,000 residing in hospitals of the New York State system.

Unfortunately such studies do not rule out the influence of other factors that may, in large part, have accounted for these results. In one well-staffed hospital where an effective treatment program had already been achieved, the introduction of drugs resulted in no measurable improvement in overall rehabilitation rates (Ellsworth and Clayton, 1960). The median length-of-stay for functionally psychotic patients, approximately 90 per cent of whom were treated with ataractic drugs, was reduced from 112 days (predrug era) to 92 days (drug era). This 20-day difference was accounted for by 3 to 5 per cent of the drug-era patients leaving the hospital in a shorter time than their predrug counterparts. This difference did not reach statistical significance. The rate of readmissions within a year after discharge increased from 25 per cent for predrug patients to 31 per cent for those who were treated when drugs were used. Sheppard et al. (1961) also found that the introduction of psychotropic drugs into their already therapeutically oriented hospital had little appreciable effect on the discharge rate of schizophrenic admissions, although 12 per cent more of them received drugs than in the New York State analysis. They conclude that ". . . the arrival of new forms of treatment frequently initiates a wave of intra-hospital activity, effects of which must be taken into account when evaluating any resulting benefits" (*ibid.*, p. 18). In general, ". . . the drugs have made it possible to change the institutional atmosphere of routine fortitude, solemn vigilance, and covert resignation to one of therapeutic enthusiasm and constructive activity" (Joint Commission Report on Mental Illness and Health, 1961, p. 57).

These conclusions suggest that the New York State hospitals, as well as some other large state mental hospitals, were excessively custodial prior to ataractic drugs. Data presented by Pollack et al. (1959, p. 41 Appendix Table 6), suggest that this was exactly the situation, and that had New York been able to achieve what some mental hospital systems were already achieving with schizophrenic patients before the advent of tranquilizing drugs, the fall in the hospital population could have occurred several years earlier. For example, the New York State hospital system had reported that only 10 per cent of all first-admission male schizophrenics were released within three months of admission, while 53 per cent had achieved a release within a year. Of the other 10 states participating in this study, an average of 29 per cent of the patients were out in three months, while an average of 70 per cent had achieved a release by the end of the year. The typical (median) patient was hospitalized about 10 months before release in New York, but required only five months hospitalization in the other states. As Brill and Patton (1959) point out, following the use of these drugs in New York, there were 10 times more patients on open wards, and a definite change in policy and optimism had occurred. For many large state hospitals, these drugs apparently resulted in an increase of therapeutic success largely because they were the vehicle that introduced the kinds of practices and policies which other hospitals had already found effective.

At this point, there is little doubt that these drugs, compared with similar placebos, result in some change in patients' behavior. There have been too many well-controlled experiments on the effects of these drugs to conclude that they have no effect at all. The problem is to discover, if possible, how much of the improvement is due to the effect of the drug itself on the patient, and how much is due to its stimulation of staff expectation and staff interaction with patients. A long-term patient, whom the staff had expected to remain essentially unchanged, may become somewhat more responsive during drug treatment. The staff, in turn, begins to respond to this change, and the patient's overall improvement arises from a complex interaction of patient-responding-to-drug, staff-responding-to-change, and patient-responding-to-change in staff interest and expectation. One may say that the drug caused the improvement because, without it, this chain of events would probably not have occurred. Others, however, would prefer to study the relative contribution of various factors in this chain of events in order to better understand the processes of recovery in schizophrenia. Unfortunately, this is an extremely difficult task, for man is a complex social animal who resists attempts to isolate the variables that influence him.

PSYCHOTHERAPY

The effectiveness of psychotherapy with hospitalized schizophrenic patients continues to be debated. Unlike what happens with chemotherapy, the nursing and ancillary staff are usually unable to communicate to the patient an expectation for change because they often do not believe in the efficacy of psychotherapy. Stevenson (1959) reports that the value of psychotherapy remains only a matter of personal conviction since there have been almost no studies of its effectiveness. "Considering the millions of dollars annually invested in it, . . . that we have almost no satisfactory studies of its results is a major scandal of our profession" (ibid., p. 120). In his survey of state and federal hospitals, Feldman (1961) found that the majority of institutions did not view the psychotherapeutic treatment of schizophrenics as particularly effective. On the other hand, some hold that psychotherapy is the treatment of choice for the mental hospital patient (Levinson and Sharof, 1958), the most potent available technique (Appleby, 1958), and the only treatment that deals with the patient's illness rather than his symptoms (Pickford and Taffel, 1958).

Recent studies, however, have raised serious doubts that psychotherapy with the schizophrenic is the treatment of choice. When compared with adequate resocialization and activity programs for the schizophrenic patient, Walker and Kelley (1960) could find no evidence that the addition of psychotherapy itself was effective. In their study, the 44 admission psychotic patients (mostly schizophrenic) who received short-term psychotherapy improved no more than the 38 similar patients who received none. Although this study included some patients who were seen in brief supportive therapy sessions, there was no evidence that patients who were worked with intensively improved more than patients who were seen only briefly. Neither was there any evidence that experienced psychotherapists had any better results than those less experienced. A three-year follow-up of these same patients (Walker and Kelley, 1963) revealed no essential differences in freedom from symptoms nor in employment for those who had received therapy as compared with those who had not, although 13 per cent more of the therapy patients had been readmitted to the hospital during this time.

A second study by Anker and Walsh (1961) involved 56 chronically hospitalized schizophrenic patients. The two treatment approaches studied were three hours per week of group therapy sessions, and three hours in which groups engaged in the production of a play. All patients took part in their assigned groups for one full year. Only the activity variable (play production with or without the addition of group psychotherapy) produced significant and consistent behavioral improvement, with group psychotherapy alone producing only minor positive changes.

Two other studies, however, find some evidence that group psychotherapy with hospitalized psychotics (mostly schizophrenics) is related to hospital release. Roos (1961) finds that although the combination of group psychotherapy and insulin treatment produces no measurable behavioral change, as compared with insulin treatment alone, the patients in group therapy are more likely to leave the hospital earlier. This result is in direct contrast to the study cited earlier (Walker and Kelley, 1960) in which those patients receiving psychotherapy remained in the hospital significantly longer than those assigned to activity programs.

Some positive evidence for the value of group psychotherapy was found in a second study with "moderately chronic" psychotic patients reported by Vernallis and Reinert (1961). In this study, 6 of the 30 patients receiving group psychotherapy were out of the hospital at the end of the 18-month study period (8 others had left but were rehospitalized), while only one control patient remained out (10 others returned). The fact that less than half of the therapy group left the hospital during the 18-month period, and that most of them subsequently returned, raises some serious questions concerning the overall effectiveness of this hospital. In other hospitals, similar or better results have been reported without the use of psychotherapy.

That so few carefully controlled studies on the effectiveness of psychotherapy with hospitalized patients have been reported is indeed surprising, especially since psychotherapy itself is such a time-consuming and costly procedure. In many ways the practice of psychotherapy has become functionally autonomous in that it continues to be practiced for its own sake with very little attempt being made to systematically evaluate it. Lacking meaningful relationships with others, some "purchase" this kind of relationship from a professionally trained therapist (Schofield, 1964). Also, McPartland and Richart (1966) report that the role of patienthood is more likely to be adopted by those who gain little satisfaction from such roles as parent, spouse, employee, and the like. Unable to find help or satisfaction in their lives, many people become patients in order to find someone who cares for and listens to them. The role of patienthood, then, may often represent a substitute for more unsatisfactory role relationships. Unaware of this possibility, many therapists have probably helped perpetuate the role of patienthood in their clients. It is of interest that time-limited therapy may offer the advantage of crisis intervention and counseling without the disadvantages of prolonged patienthood that time-unlimited psychotherapy encourages (Levy, 1966). As late as 1964, Cross could find only nine studies evaluating the outcome of psychotherapy with adequate controls. He concluded that the efficacy of the psychotherapeutic approach ". . . has not been scientifically demonstrated beyond some reasonable doubt" (Cross, 1964, p. 416). The assumption underlying the psychotherapeutic approach is that the etiology of schizophrenic reactions is to be found in the unresolved emotional problems and conflicts of the patient. Perhaps this assumption is not basically correct. The results of psychotherapy may also be restricted because its use as a technique does not necessarily bring about a generalized expectation for recovery on the part of the hospital staff. Without this essential sociopsychological ingredient, the impact of this approach on patient recovery remains uneven.

SOCIOPSYCHOLOGICAL APPROACHES TO TREATMENT

To identify those social situational variables that underlie the patient's response to hospitalization those conditions that lead to chronicity, apathy, and withdrawal might well be examined. Bockoven (1956) has outlined in detail the factors leading to the decline of the small therapeutic hospitals of the 1840's, and the rise of today's large, impersonal, custodial institutions. His writings on this subject leave little doubt that the "hopelessly insane" person of the 1900's was a joint product of such factors as professional pessimism, large impersonal institutions that forced the patient to withdraw, a pessimistic emphasis on "mental-illness-as-a-disease" for which there was no known cure, and the loss of human dignity for the patient who became a passive object to be kept clean and alive, and to be autopsied carefully upon his death. The concept of earlier moral treatment, on the other hand, was based on the assumption that the natural course of mental illness was toward recovery, unless impeded by the apathy, boredom, and impersonalization induced by institutionalization.

Cultural values in the United States changed markedly between the 1840's and 1920's (see Bockoven, 1957). The moral treatment was based on the nineteenth-century concept of the dignity of man, as manifested by the establishment of free public schools and libraries. The social Darwinism of the 1890's, which taught that only the fit should survive, helped to reverse the philosophy and practice of "I am my brother's keeper." The social value of conformity reached its peak during the pre-World War I era. This was paralleled in the country's institutions by lack of tolerance of nonconformity and adverse reaction to the patient showing deviant behavior. As long as the patient was a conforming nonentity, he escaped aggressive practices that attendants sometimes used in controlling nonconformity. Under such circumstances, it is not surprising that the institutions of the early twentieth century contained thousands of regressed, apathetic patients whose main goal in life was to conform.

Separating an individual from his community and placing him in institutional settings is also an important factor in encouraging the development of certain behaviors once thought to be a function of the patient's illness. After a careful review of the detailed accounts of the behavioral changes following institutionalization in orphanages, TB sanitariums, displaced persons camps, and the like, Caudill et al. (1952) conclude: "In general, the accounts of behavior in these types of settings all stress the phenomena, so many of which are noted in hospitalized mental patients, of apathy and depersonalization, regression, denial of reality . . ." (p. 332). Deane (1961), who had had himself admitted to a psychiatric ward, reported experiencing many of the symptoms associated with mental illness. He experienced withdrawal from active participation, indulgence in fantasy, strong feelings of hostility in reaction to "little things," and a great sense of boredom and apathy. York's observation (1955, p. 346) that regressive behavior is in no small part a result of the institutional environment, seems no longer a point for serious debate.

The belief that the mental patient was a "sick" person unable to assume much responsibility for himself also had far-reaching implications. It implied that the controls for this irresponsible patient had to be imposed from without. The institutions developed well-ordered routines that removed from the patient the responsibility for decision making. What the patient would eat, do, say, wear, and think were all decided for him. As a consequence, an observable deficit in many long-term hospitalized patients is their inability and unwillingness to make decisions for themselves. Early experience with patient-government programs, for example, revealed that the long-term patient initially was reluctant to take responsibility for making recommendations and decisions. Taking away from the patient the responsibility for decision making is still another example of how institutions helped to produce the dependent, withdrawn patient, ill-prepared to assume an independent role in the outside world.

Patients, after prolonged institutionalization, are often unable to make the transition to community life without a great deal of trauma. Something in prolonged institutionalization apparently teaches the patient to become excessively dependent, and to find the structured environment more satisfying than "freedom." In one rehabilitation program with chronically hospitalized patients, Miller (1954, p. 354) observed, ". . . every patient who is discharged from the hospital became dramatically more sick as the time to leave approached." Downing (1958) suggests that psychotic behavior is maintained or imitated by the chronic patient to counter the possibility of excessive anxiety associated with release. Prolonged separation of the patient from the outside community creates additional problems that must be handled. The development of half-way houses, foster homes, and outpatient clinics are examples of recent attempts to ease the patient's transition into the community.

During the last decade, many of the regressive influences of custodialism have been reversed. Some of these changes seem to have been initiated through the introduction of tranquilizing drugs. The pessimism of the staff and the low expectation for patient recovery have been replaced with increased optimism. The violent ward of the 1940's has largely disappeared. Attendants trained in handling aggressive patients found this skill to be increasingly of less value in the mental hospital setting. The patient himself became more approachable and easier to accept. As a result, the staff found themselves changing their attitudes about the mentally ill. Rather than regarding the patient as a person not to be trusted, they began to feel that he should be encouraged to develop more responsibility for himself. If the ward staff communicate to the patient that they *expect* change, as suggested earlier, the patient's reaction to this expectation may largely determine the extent of his rehabilitation.

The widespread acceptance and use of ataractic drugs actually provides some excellent clues concerning the characteristics of those treatment approaches most likely to be accepted by staff and patients alike. The ease with which these drugs were introduced into the mental hospital suggests that mental hospital personnel basically ascribe to the theory of organic etiology in mental illness. Illness and drugs have traditionally gone together in the field of medicine. Also, the "patient" who is in the "hospital" for "treatment" usually finds medication acceptable. To him, it often means that something specific is being done to help him. In prescribing drugs, the psychiatrist-as-physician is playing a role more in harmony with the patient's background and training. A treatment approach that enhances already established attitudes of both patients and staff will be much more readily accepted than a treatment approach requiring a new orientation. This largely explains why the development of effective social rehabilitation techniques has progressed so unevenly in this country. If one behaves as *if* mental illness is essentially a physiological disturbance, he seriously limits the extent to which he can employ or participate in some of the newer sociological approaches.

Unlike tranquilizing drugs, the introduction of such treatment concepts as the therapeutic community require a drastic change in patient and staff roles (Brown and Greenblatt, 1955; Cumming and Cumming, 1957; Jones, 1956; Greenblatt, 1957; Schwartz, M. S. 1957; and Vitale, 1964). Because of the rigidity of staff roles, a feature of the bureaucratic institution, hospital personnel are either unwilling or unable to alter their relationships with each other or with their patients. It has been found, also, that the patient himself comes to the hospital with clearly defined role expectations for himself and staff. The majority of patients, for example, come to the hospital expecting to play a passive, compliant role in relating to a magically healing doctor (Levinson and Gallagher, 1964). Thus the patient through his own role expectations is instrumental in promoting the traditionality of staff roles.

The concept of the patient as an active participant in his own treatment, however, seems to be one of the fundamental role changes associated with the development of the therapeutic hospital (Brown and Greenblatt, 1955; Gilbert and Levinson, 1957). Rather than a passive object who receives treatment, the patient becomes a surprisingly responsible human being who can be treated, in large part, as if he were normal. Increasingly, he is expected to assume the duties and responsibilities that normal human beings exercise in their daily living. One of the fundamental assumptions of this book is that staff expectation of responsible patient behavior is one of the basic ingredients of an effective treatment program. It is especially significant that a new approach to treatment built on this concept has recently emerged in the form of "reality therapy" (Glasser, 1965).

Despite the apparent attractiveness of such concepts as "patient as active participant," "patient responsibility," and an increase in "shared problem solving," little research has been conducted on the impact of these concepts on treatment effectiveness. As discussed earlier, our own research (Ellsworth and Stokes, 1963) has suggested that the staff of a high-turnover hospital are more apt to regard the patient as an active participant in his illness and his recovery than the staff of a low-turnover hospital. In this study it was also found that as the discharge rate of the low turn-over hospital increased, the staff of that hospital began to reject the assumption that patients were sick because of factors outside their control, and instead adopted the belief that patients were active participants in their illness and recovery. The only other study known to this writer in this area is the current Veterans Administration Psychiatric Research Project by Gurel et al. (1964), who found that the more effective mental hospital is one characterized as "non-traditional." Hospitals that tried new programs and staffing patterns tended to be most effective.

EXPECTATION AS THE COMMON THERAPEUTIC INGREDIENT OF ALL SUCCESSFUL TREATMENT APPROACHES

In this chapter the thesis is outlined that all successful treatment approaches, whether they be physiological or psychosocial, have a common therapeutic ingredient. The manner in which the *expectation* for change and improvement is brought into play represents the basic therapeutic ingredient of all successful treatment approaches. Insulin, electroshock, or milieu therapy, then, simply represent different vehicles by which this expectation is introduced and responded to by both patients and staff.

This expectation for change and improvement is a necessary but not sufficient condition underlying successful treatment approaches. In order for this expectation to become believable, change must occur. For a patient who receives medication, change is indeed experienced. If this change is reacted to by the staff, then the previously outlined cycle of patient-response-to-staff-reaction-to-change is initiated. Under these conditions, the expectation for change and improvement becomes believable for both staff and patient. If change begins to occur but is not responded

to by staff, this cycle is short-circuited and little improvement is likely
to occur. One strategy for insuring that change does not continue is
simply for staff not to have expected, and therefore not to look for, nor
respond to, initial patient change.

In the psychosocial approaches, the change agent is more difficult
to identify. Actually, as suggested in Chapter 2, change occurs continually, for no patient remains the same from day to day. Confronted
with the behavior of the staff, patients do respond to their demands. If
staff expectations are communicated through both words and actions,
then the patient is more likely to change in response to these clearly
communicated expectations. On the other hand, staff who tell a patient
they expect him to behave responsibly, while at the same time they put
him on a locked ward, hardly communicate the conviction of their
expectations that he will indeed behave responsibly.

So much has been written about the characteristics of the therapeutic milieu that the concept has become confusing and difficult to
apply. In addition to staff expectation and reaction to patient change,
the expectation for responsible behavior is perhaps more strongly emphasized in the milieu approaches than in the more traditional therapeutic techniques. Many staff and patients still believe that patients
cannot (or should not) assume responsibility for their behavior because
they are "sick." If one assumes that sick behavior is beyond the control
of the patient, then the expectation for irresponsible behavior becomes
valid. Not infrequently one hears patients excuse certain behavior by
claiming to "possess" schizophrenia, mental illness, or the like. Treating
patients as if they were capable of normal behavior has already been
identified as one of the attitudes conveyed by the moral treatment staff
of the 1840's. Such an attitude is clearly evident in today's more therapeutically effective teams.

In addition to the expectation for responsible behavior, the milieu
approaches also emphasize the expectation that the patient become
an active participant in his life and in the decisions concerning himself.
Many staff, for example, make it clear to the patient that it is his actions
that result in a transfer to a closed ward, a legal commitment to the
hospital, and so on. Custodial mental hospitals, whose staff assumed that
patients' behavior was beyond patient control, developed methods for
controlling patient behavior. The staff of therapeutic milieu programs
attempt to help patients develop their own internal controls. As suggested earlier, a patient's active participation in the decisions concerning
himself also enhances his own commitment to these decisions.

To involve the patient in the decisions concerning himself also implies staff respect for the dignity of the patient. Staff expectancies

should be in keeping with the patient's capability, for to expect a severely withdrawn patient to assume a full-time job outside the hospital after a few days' treatment is obviously unrealistic. To expect such a patient to become increasingly less withdrawn and more outgoing, however, seems necessary in producing these kinds of changes. As the patient finds himself able to live up to staff expectations, he is likely to begin to regard himself as increasingly worthwhile in his own eyes. Realistic staff expectancies, communicating respect for the dignity and values of the patient, are typically found in successful milieu approaches.

The basic ingredient of all successful therapeutic approaches, then, is the successfully communicated expectation for change and improvement. Successful communication of this expectation depends on both staff optimism for success as well as their ability to communicate this expectation in both their words and actions. In addition, the milieu approaches to patient rehabilitation emphasize: (1) an expectation for responsible behavior; (2) an expectation for active participation on the part of the patient, and (3) an awareness of the values, and concern for the dignity, of the patient. To expect either too little or too much of the patient is to communicate to him his failure as a person.

The quality of leadership in the milieu approaches is critical since the kind of attitude changes outlined above are not easily achieved. Also, staff cannot communicate to the patient their expectation for responsible behavior or active participation in problem solving unless the team leader treats his own staff in this way. To do less robs staff of dignity and respect, and they in turn are likely to respond to the patient in the same way. These problems in professional leadership are considered in detail in Chapter 4.

SUMMARY

Specific treatment approaches, such an insulin coma and EST, have typically had their maximum success when they were first introduced into the hospital setting. The basis for this success may be attributed primarily to the expectation for recovery communicated to the patient, rather than to the specific treament itself. This sociopsychological interpretation of the treatment process was also used in analyzing the success of the recently introduced tranquilizing drugs. It was suggested that these drugs have had their greatest impact in the large, poorly staffed hospitals, primarily because they have brought about a change in the staff's expectation for recovery. In well-staffed hospitals, where expectation for recovery was already high, the introduction of these drugs has had less impact on patient rehabilitation.

The effectiveness of psychotherapy has not been clearly demonstrated with hospitalized schizophrenics. Psychotherapy, unlike other treatment approaches, may not stimulate a generalized staff expectancy for patient recovery, and the absence of this expectation may account for the uneven results of psychotherapy. With hospitalized schizophrenics this technique may lack demonstrated effectiveness for other reasons as well, such as wide differences in the quality of interaction between therapists and patients, or working with the patient apart from his social living situations.

Increased attention has recently been paid to the sociopsychological processes associated with a patient's regression and recovery. Impersonality, regimentation, and low expectation for recovery have led to regression in patients' behavioral adjustment, a regression once thought to be a function of the disease process itself. Attempts have been made to alter the hospital milieu so that the disabling social conditions are minimized, while at the same time the ingredients believed to enhance recovery are emphasized. There seems to be some agreement concerning those sociopsychological conditions that facilitate rehabilitation, yet there has been little research to indicate which of these conditions is really important in the recovery process itself. In the absence of such evidence, and because of rigidity in staff roles in many hospital settings, the drastic changes that many feel are necessary to achieve a therapeutic milieu have not occurred.

4

The Psychiatric Aide in the
Mental Hospital

Studies of the typical state mental hospital have revealed that the rehabilitation and treatment staff have almost no direct personal impact
on the patients under their care. In a 2,400-bed hospital, for example,
only 15 per cent of patients, in a given week, received any personal
attention from nurses, psychiatrists, psychologists, social workers, activity
therapists, or chaplains (Gusick, 1957). Of the 192,000 waking hours
for this group of 2,400 patients, less than 3 per cent was spent in the
presence of professionally trained staff. The largest employee group
having direct contact with patients are the psychiatric aides, and yet,
because they lack professional training, they are rarely encouraged to
take an active role in rehabilitation. Even if there were enough hospital
psychiatrists to meet the standards of the American Psychiatric Association, the acute patient would be seen about 50 minutes a week, the
continued-treatment patient about 10 minutes a week. Faced with such
data, the Joint Commission on Mental Illness and Health concluded
that the long-cherished belief that a competent doctor of medicine
should personally attend each sick person must, perforce, be abandoned
(Joint Commission Report, 1961, p. 252).

The greatest untapped manpower resource for direct patient contact
is the psychiatric aide. Though he is most numerous, he is also least well
trained, lowest in the professional hierarchy, lowest on the pay scale, and
seemingly most resistant to change. Yet, the aide exerts a powerful
influence on the programs of the mental hospital. He can make or break
a particular treatment program. In his relationship with patients, he
can create an atmosphere of suspicion and distrust, or one of warmth
and dignity. In most mental hospitals, however, there has been an inability, to a large extent, to constructively use the manpower resources
of the psychiatric aide as an active participant in the hospital programs.
A recent survey (Public Health Service, 1964, p. 11) found that over

two thirds of aides did not attend any meetings; instead they spent the majority of their time dressing patients and keeping them clean, giving medication, and serving food. At the same time, only 7 per cent of aides surveyed felt the need for more communication and team work between staff members, and only 2 per cent wanted more responsibility in working with patients. In short, the aide has a great deal of contact with the patient in nursing-care activities, yet he rarely becomes an active participant in the treatment team.

Turning to the aide for help in working more therapeutically with patients, he is apt to be found unable or unwilling to cooperate fully. When he is asked to spend more time interacting with patients, instead he is found continuing to visit with co-workers. When he is asked to attend and participate in team meetings, he is reluctant to speak up. In one small, well-staffed hospital, for example, the average aide spent only about 20 per cent of his time talking with, or doing things with patients in the off-ward activity areas (Ellsworth et al., 1960). Most of his time was spent talking with another aide, reading, passively watching, or involving himself in solitary activity for his own amusement. As compared with any other hospital group, the aides express the strongest commitment to the custody and control of the patient (Mishler, 1955). Furthermore, the aide apparently feels comfortable in his role of minimal therapeutic responsibility (Lawton, 1964).

At one time in mental hospitals, the aide's role as custodian was understandable. Viewing many patients as relatively unlikely to leave the institution, the professional staff abandoned them. What was assigned to the aide was the caretaker role. Before tranquilizing drugs, these personnel developed skills in quieting the disturbed patients and running an orderly ward. With the introduction of tranquilizing medication, many aides found their control skills no longer valued. As hospitals shifted from custody to rehabilitation, the caretaker role of the aide was no longer appropriate. And as the patient himself became a more active participant in treatment planning, and more responsible for his own behavior, the importance of the aides' traditional role decreased further.

Encouraging the aide to play a more active role in patient rehabilitation has been only minimally successful. Telling him that he is now an important team member does not necessarily result in his participating actively in treatment planning (Artiss, 1962, p. 9). Although given special training courses, he seems unwilling or unable to put into practice what he has learned in the classroom (Morgan and Hall, 1950). As a matter of fact, such training often succeeds in replacing warmth and genuineness with hesitancy and aloofness (Morgan and Gibson, 1959). Meeting the demand for more help by doubling the aide-to-patient ratio, one study (Gutenkauf and Lundin, 1958) found no increase in aide-patient interaction. Rather there developed instead: (1) intense criticism of other aides and accusations of favoritism; (2) scapegoating in order to protect the in-group clique from criticism; (3) the selection of individual patients as one's personal property; (4) increased conflict between shifts with each blaming the other for failure to do its share of the work; and finally, (5) a demand for still more staff. In general, then, these approaches to the problem do not necessarily increase either the quality or the quantity of aide-patient interaction.

The potential for meaningful aide-patient interaction is surely present. As a matter of fact, significant interaction probably occurs more frequently than most professional staff realize. The psychiatric aide already knows that he is influential in affecting patients' behavior and attitudes. Every aide has had the experience of successfully quieting a frightened patient, talking a resistive patient into trusting and cooperating with the professional staff, or reawakening a patient's interest in working toward discharge. These personnel, in constant contact with the patient, are often the only consistently supportive influence in the patient's life. In any large institution, the patient comes into contact with some people who want to help, some who seem angry with him, some who encourage him to get better, or some who don't care. In the confusing and contradictory world of the mental hospital, the aide is often the only available person who can help the patient keep his perspective. As such, the aide knows that he is often the critical factor in determining the patient's response to hospitalization since he is frequently the only person who actually sits down and talks with the patient in a sustained relationship. The aide has always known this, but many of the professional staff are just beginning to recognize it. Although professionals have been saying for a long time that the aide is important, the aide is acutely aware that they often do not act as if they really believe what they say.

INCONSISTENT VERBAL
AND NONVERBAL COMMUNICATION
CONCERNING THE AIDE'S ROLE

Underlying the aide's inability to take a more active part in patient rehabilitation is the contradiction between what we professionals say and how we have acted in our relationship to him. Telling him that his sustained relationship with the patients is extremely important, we sit by while the aide is transferred to another ward. Attempting to give him additional recognition by calling him an important member of our team, we practically insult him by ignoring, or showing disinterest in, what he says. We tell him how interested we are in him and his development, and then fail to learn his name, his background, or what interests him in his work. Encouraging him to take initiative, we fail to defend or support him when something goes wrong. Without considering the fact that aides help patients get better, we publicly attribute patient improvement to drugs or psychotherapy. We tell the aide that the hospital could not run without him, and then pay him so little that he has to take an outside job to support his family.

Examining conditions under which aides work, one finds that the hospital also helps in communicating to him an expectation of poor performance. Most of us assume, for example, that the aide is a technically inept person who works at his job only because he can't find better employment elsewhere. Our techniques of supervision do not communicate to him that he is a responsible partner in the hospital organization. The aide is kept "on his toes" with inspection rounds, performance ratings, counseling sessions, reprimands for incidences of poor performance, and the ever present threat of expulsion if he violates an imposed system of do's and don'ts. We call him to the front office when he's done something wrong, not when he excels. Ignoring outstanding performances, we focus instead on the occasional infraction of some rule. Proclaiming our concern for adequate coverage for patients, we alter his time schedules with little regard for the aide's personal needs or preferences and shift him randomly from ward to ward. And finally, on pay day we once more communicate to him our perception of his value.

I first discovered at another hospital (see Ellsworth et al., 1960) that the aide's performance in off-ward activity areas was largely ignored. An aide was considered adequate as long as he was not abusive to patients, and not quarrelsome in his relationship with the activity therapist. Unrecognized for excelling in performance, the aide who spent most of his time working directly with his patients received no more support than the aide who sat passively, uninvolved with patients. Unable to find the time, the aides' supervisor did not participate in off-ward activity and accordingly could not support the aide's interaction with patients. On the ward he was sometimes told to "get busy doing something" when he sat down to talk with the patients, with the clear implication that talking to patients was a waste of time. Under these circumstances, the aide had no real incentive to develop and practice effective interaction skills, nor was there any consistent message given to him that this was even desired.

Preoccupied with the importance of drugs in changing patient behavior, the professional staff imply that what the aide does with the patient is relatively unimportant. Lacking knowledge about what happens to the patient throughout the 24 hours, we assume that what we do with the patient is the cause of the patient's change. When a psychotherapy patient is presented to a team conference, we focus on what happened in the therapy hour and thereby communicate the assumption that the patient's other interactions are not therapeutic (Kennard, 1957).

Lacking recognition and support, then, it is not surprising that most aides do not play an active and responsible role. When offered the invitation to become more actively involved, however, the aide often ignores us. Perhaps the aide already obtains certain rewards and satisfaction for playing his traditional passive, custodial role. We need to better understand how the aide perceives his role and his relationship to the professional staff.

THE AIDE PEER GROUP CULTURE

Certain traditions, incompatible with the practices of a therapeutic hospital, have become part of the aide's culture. Traditionally ignored by the professional staff, the aide identifies primarily with his own in-group and rejects the values of the professional staff. This in-group identification is reinforced by the aides' own peers. At first, if a new aide does not adopt the values of the peer culture, strong pressures are brought to bear. If this fails, the new aide is likely to find himself transferred to an undesirable ward and will probably leave the institution (Belnap, 1956, p. 187).

Perceiving the staff as parasites (*ibid.*, p. 76) who take credit for all accomplishments (*ibid.*, p. 153), the aides nevertheless feel that *they* are the ones who do all the real work (*ibid.*, p. 76). It was recently found that some aides believe that they have more of a therapeutic influence on patients than anyone else (Strauss, 1964). It was also clear from this report that the author could not accept this as possible. These differences in perception serve only to further alienate the professional staff and aide groups, and to strengthen the aide's identification with his own in-group.

Although many regard the aide as relatively uninfluential in the patient's life, a closer examination of the traditional ward culture has revealed the extent of the aides' real influence. Aides have developed effective techniques of rewarding desirable patient behavior: The status of a favored person was given to the patient who conformed. He received extra tobacco, better clothing, ground privileges, desirable work assignments, a pleasant room, and so on. Patients experienced the consequences of deviation from acceptable behavior, and quickly learned what was expected of them. Unfortunately, some of these codes for aide behavior, such as, "Never speak to a patient except to tell him what to do," are largely contradictory to modern psychiatric concepts of treatment since "the control of the patient is emphasized at the expense of his improvement" (Dunham and Weinberg, 1960, p. 248).

The hospital's formal organization charges the professional staff with the responsibility of managing a patient's life, both in decision making and treatment planning. In reality, however, the aide often controls the professional staff rather than being controlled by them. Belnap (1956), for example, discovered that the manner in which aides described the patient's behavior to the physician almost always determined the outcome of decisions regarding EST, loss of privileges, or transfer to another building. Thus, the aide could legitimately promise the patient that unacceptable behavior would result in some form of punishment, thereby introducing an effective method of control. Belnap (ibid., p. 94) also discovered that physicians' orders were often carried out only if the attendant decided to carry them out. Thus, the exercising of authority, formally given to the professional staff, was often actually under the control of the ward attendants.

The foregoing discussion suggests one final point in understanding the aides' reluctance to adopt the values of the professional staff and to assume a more active part in patient rehabilitation. This is the question of power. In an authoritarian relationship, one group has been given formal responsibility for directing the treatment program, and another group is delegated to carry it out. The power, however, lies not with the authority figure, but with those who are directed by him. An aide may choose whether or not to follow a directive and whether or not to support or undercut a program. As long as the aide is not part of the professional staff culture, he will assume little responsibility for working within the framework of a program proposed by the professional staff. The extent to which the aide identifies with, and feels part of, the treatment team determines the extent to which he will assume responsibility for his role in the program. Unless he gains enough satisfaction from a genuine relationship with the professional staff, he will be unlikely to give up the power gratification to be found in a so-called "subservient" role.

BUREAUCRACY AND STATUS HIERARCHY IN THE MENTAL HOSPITAL

Many features of the mental hospital make it extremely difficult to break down the barriers between the professional staff and the psychiatric aide group. The goals of the mental hospital are several, of which patient rehabilitation is sometimes one of the least important (Ewalds, 1964). The elaborate set of institutional rules and regulations communicates that patients and staff should meet the needs of the system, rather than that the system should meet patient and staff needs. Proposed solutions to problems are more apt to be those that do not violate an established regulation, not those that are best for the patient.

When the institution's operations become complex certain rules and regulations must be adopted to facilitate decision making and limit possible alternatives. The institution thus becomes bureaucratic in nature (Kahne, 1959). Decision making, communication, control, and policy coordination are formalized within a pyramiding chain of impersonal authority. Those at the top, because of their status, exercise direct control in granting or withholding requests that come to them up the chain of command. Kahne (*ibid.*) points out that one of the emerging status symbols in the United States is whether or not a person has the authority to directly influence or exercise control over others. In mental hospitals, both functional and scalar status among clinical personnel increase in direct proportion to the distance from the patients, and in inverse proportion to the amount of time spent with them. Many decisions concerning a particular patient cannot be made by the ward personnel, who are most intimately familiar with the patient, because certain alternatives may be contrary to hospital rules. Thus, blind adherence to rules and regulations has come to substitute for good clinical judgment.

Specialized roles are also developed within the bureaucratic institution. Specialization is accompanied by status conflicts between services and by problems of divided loyalties. One is often forced to choose between what is good for the patient and what is good for one's own department. This problem is increasingly recognized by the nursing service. Traditionally, personnel were arbitrarily shifted and rotated from ward to ward with little concern for continuing relationships between personnel and patients. As a matter of fact, the reason for moving personnel was often that of preventing too close an identification with patients. A nurse or an aide, for example, might begin to play an effective role on a ward because he had become identified and familiar with the needs of the patients. To the dismay of both staff and patients, often he would be moved to another ward. Increasingly, some nursing departments are willing to establish relatively permanent teams and to let the nurse and aide become identified with their ward and its patients. A great deal of ambivalence remains, however, about the wisdom of this policy, especially when the ward personnel begin to identify more with the ward program than with their own service. This problem occurs in every department of the hospital. The occupational therapist, for example, is usually identified with his clinic and his service. Patients are delivered to him for therapy and he rarely becomes involved in the plans that the ward staff develop for their patients. Ward problems are foreign to him and represent a separate world to him. Concerned about the evaluation his supervisor will make of him and his status among his own co-workers, he becomes administratively oriented. Such problems as the number of treatments his clinic administers during the month, and how it compares with other clinics in the hospital come to occupy his attention.

Because of such situations, various departments begin to compete for the better-adjusted patients. The various services develop jealously guarded functions that other departments must be kept from encroaching upon. The personnel become concerned about defining and justifying their functions as "therapy." Representing a threat to their share of the highly prized therapy pie, the aide's assistance is resisted by many activity therapists. In the rigidly structured mental hospital, there is much solicitude over whether or not a work detail of patients should be under Occupational Therapy, Industrial Therapy, Manual Arts Therapy, or the Engineers; whether or not a volley ball game becomes the rightful function of Recreational Service, Special Service, Corrective Therapy, or Physical Therapy; and whether or not a department can get better patients, more budget, more space, and more therapists. The primary concern is the department's own status and importance rather than co-ordination of efforts to help the patient. In the highly specialized hospital, unfortunately more attention is paid to who does what, rather than what gets done.

John and Elaine Cumming (1957) have attempted to analyze the process by which successful programs are introduced. Reporting that effective programs are impossible without a high level of staff-to-staff planning, they found, instead, "caste-like hierarchies" between professional and subprofessional staff. A great deal of effort was required to break down status barriers between professional and ward personnel. In their experience, a coordinated staff, engrossed in the process of planning programs for patients, exercises a great impact upon the ward itself.

They conclude, "We doubt that integrated therapeutic ward programs are possible without a high level of staff-to-staff planning" (*ibid.*, p. 58). Unless these traditional hierarchies are broken down, the problems requiring the most attention are likely to be those which center around the power struggle.

A psychiatrist may begin his institutional career by identifying and pointing out desired changes to those whose duty it is to modify various therapeutic practices. He discovers that, "His decisions concerning ward situations have no 'legitimacy' because the nursing hierarchy believes that he knows nothing about a mental hospital" (Cumming and Cumming, 1957, p. 54). The struggle for power cuts both ways, and reduces the effectiveness of coordinating problem solving at all levels. At this point, some psychiatrists choose to retreat into such specialist functions as diagnosis and traditional psychiatric treatment where they are clearly perceived and recognized as experts. Thus, in the highly bureaucratic hospital, many psychiatrists abdicate their role as effective social therapists.

In the traditional hospital, even in the professional aspects of his work, much of the authority and control has been taken out of the psychiatrist's hands. If his hospital continues to hold disposition staffs through which each patient must pass, the decision to discharge a patient is not really his to make. If his chief of staff continues to review all his correspondence with relatives, the hospital administration communicates to the psychiatrist that they do not quite trust his professional judgment. The hospital tells the psychiatrist to develop an effective team, but withholds from him authority and responsibility. The psychiatrist becomes a figurehead. Neither the psychiatrist nor his team associates invest much in treatment planning if their decisions can be arbitrarily reversed by someone unfamiliar with the patient and his problems.

In those hospitals where autocratic control is being relinquished, the possibility of developing new and creative programs is enhanced. Instead of maintaining the status quo and adhering to safe, standard, but largely unproductive practices, some institutions are beginning to allow the decision making and planning to occur at the ward staff level. In general, however, the lack of delegated authority typical of most institutions continues to prevent the development of effective leadership, and remains a constant source of irritation to most psychiatrists.

Many of the problems that underlie the difficulties of the aide in becoming a full partner of the treatment team, then, are a function of the bureaucratic structure of the mental hospital. Caught in a situation where the competition for status, power, and prestige are high, the aide, as low man in the hierarchy, is likely to play a passive role. As suggested earlier, his role in the traditional hospital already encompasses far more power than most personnel realize. To ask him to give this up in exchange for verbally stated but rarely fulfilled promises of team membership is expecting too much.

PROBLEMS IN PROFESSIONAL LEADERSHIP

The difficulties arising out of status hierarchies in the bureaucratic organization of the mental hospital have caused at least one writer to question, "Can anything less than a social revolution within the hospital remedy these ills?" (Greenblatt, 1955, p. 148). And yet, progress has been made. For example, many large institutions have adopted the unit system by creating small autonomous hospitals-within-the-hospital. This shifts the locus of control down toward the ward or unit level. The development of the team concept is also an acknowledgment of the potential contribution of all personnel who work with the patient. The establishment of patient government has involved the patient as a more active participant in the affairs of the institution. Through innovations such as these, a downward shift is occurring in the control that once rested exclusively with those at the top.

Not all decision making can be delegated, for there are many administrative and general policy decisions that are best made by those at the top. Any decision, however, affecting the welfare of the patient is best made with the active participation of those who are closest to the patient and his problems. Decisions about particular patients should be left to the ward team if one wishes to enhance the ". . . opportunity for spontaniety and face to face relations between patients and ward nurses, aides, occupational therapists, recreational personnel, etc." (Kahne, 1959, p. 367). Today's decentralized teams, supported in planning for the discharge of their own patients, are releasing many patients who would not previously have been discharged. Many of them are making adequate community adjustments. Usually these are patients who develop excellent work habits and satisfactory relationship patterns, but who continue to show some residual symptomatology. For such patients, the ward staff who know them well experience no real problems of pessimistic uncertainty in planning for their discharge. Such patients, however, a few years ago, would not have been presented to an administrative/professional staff for discharge.

Part of the tradition of the bureaucratic organization, however, is the presumption of limited competence on the part of those in the lower levels of the hospital hierarchy. It is usual for the decision making to be located furthest from the events it affects. The results of these long and complex lines of communication and control are that "... the enthusiasm accompanying a new idea wilts into listless apathy during the trip 'through channels'" (*ibid.*, p. 368). The institution, therefore, must be willing to take the risks inherent in shifting downward the authority and responsibility for decisions affecting the welfare of patients. The institution must be willing to risk occasional mistakes in order to gain the benefits of shared problem solving at the ward level, and must further be prepared to support original and creative planning that will, at times, deviate from the traditions and customs of the institution.

The problem in all this is that simply shifting the responsibility downward does not necessarily insure shared problem solving at the ward level. Few professional staff members have had the training necessary to develop involved participation among all team members. In fact, the training of most professionals has had the opposite effect, for they tend to develop an image of themselves as experts in their own fields. The psychiatrist has developed specialized skills only after years of training and experience, and has become a legitimate expert in diagnosis, somatic treatment, and psychotherapy. Expected to function in areas in which they are not specialists, however, few psychiatrists can develop and successfully put into operation a coordinated therapeutic program. One of the basic requirements, strangely enough, is that he enhance the role of expertness among his team members by involving them in shared problem solving. As long as our graduate and postgraduate schools in this country continue to prepare psychiatrists (as well as psychologists and social workers) for the role of individual psychotherapy and private practice, the professional will enter the mental hospital highly ambivalent about initiating a genuine partnership with his ward staff.

One of the clearest examples of the professional staff's ambivalence about sharing with the aide and nurse the role of active team participant is observed in "team" meetings. Most mental hospital administrators acknowledge that the team concept is desirable because: (1) It facilitates the exchange of information and planning between status groups; (2) it more actively involves those personnel who have intimate patient contact; and (3) it motivates these personnel to work more effectively with their patients because their ideas are elicited and attended to. Very few teams, however, actually function in such a way that its members work as a cohesive, communicating, interdependent unit. Pointing out that the well-organized team does not occur by chance or administrative fiat, Howard (1960) suggests that it can be achieved only when the team leader is committed to the concept of team function and is willing to support a "painful growing process" on the part of the team members. Becoming involved with nonprofessional personnel in a relationship of this kind threatens the professional's perception of his own "expertness," for among his team members he may well find that there are some who are more expert than he with regard to some patients. Aides, for example, who work with a patient daily, sometimes develop an understanding exceeding that of the psychiatrist, and their ideas are often as productive as those of the psychiatrist himself (Cumming and Cumming, 1957, p. 71). The aide, most intimately familiar with the patient's day-to-day behavior and feelings, can become a valuable asset in any treatment planning. In a cohesive team, the ideas of the aides and nurses are highly valued. The psychiatrist who has been able to establish give-and-take communication with his staff often finds that the payoff for him is one of working with unexpectedly creative and dedicated people.

Although most professional staff make some attempt to play a role of team leader, they do it with a good deal of reservation. Having been taught that psychiatry is the practice of medicine, many a psychiatrist looks upon the team concept as the practice of medicine "by majority vote." Having been given the medicolegal responsibility for all his patients, he is apt to feel that everything in the patient's life is a psychiatric, and therefore a medical, matter. Under these circumstances, the team leader is reluctant to participate in shared planning because he views himself as the only real authority. In analyzing team meetings, Mouratides (1960) found that actual decisions about patients had been made before the meeting was held, and that "team" meetings were largely an empty ritual.

The role of team facilitator is difficult to practice for almost all professionals, and impossible for most. First of all, it requires a conviction that one's own best efforts are with and through others, and a concern about such problems as: (1) motivating the ward personnel; (2) providing them with a framework in which they can work comfortably and effectively; (3) supporting them both verbally and nonverbally; and (4) encouraging mutual discussion in program planning. Cherished and traditional beliefs must be reexamined, for treatment responsibility no longer belongs solely to the medical staff (Jones, 1956). The status hierarchy, with the doctor at its head, must be "flattened out" (Jones and Rapaport, 1957). This is unusually difficult for the psychiatrist to accept, however, for the belief that his best efforts are through others is in contradiction to his cherished concept of the doctor-patient relationship (Brown and Greenblatt, 1955).

Having been taught that treatment is ordered, prescribed, and directed, many new psychiatrists give up in disgust after attempting to introduce program and role changes. The ward staff have already experienced others before him, each with his own ideas, plans, and expectations. Each request for new changes implies that the ward staff's previous methods and efforts are no longer adequate. The ward staff are likely to see the new psychiatrist, particularly the psychiatric resident, as someone who will soon abandon them. The ward staff must be made to feel that the team leader has a basic commitment to them and that he respects their experience and ideas. Effective problem solving has got to be a two-way process, the team leader being taught by, as well as teaching, his staff. Only by genuinely sharing the decision-making can the professional hope to succeed in helping the team reach its therapeutic potential and enhance its commitment in carrying out "our" decisions as compared with carrying out "his" decisions.

THE ROAD AHEAD

In a book entitled *The Human Side of Enterprise*, McGregor (1960) suggests an approach in personnel development that is extremely pertinent to the hospital situation. Although written for industrial managers, the book could be paraphrased to describe equally well the role of the nonprofessional in any rehabilitation setting.

McGregor's main thesis is that the key to the growth of shared human enterprise is the creation of a climate conducive to that development. He suggests that the indifferent, irresponsible, uncooperative employee is a product of management's basic attitudes toward the employee. These attitudes, in turn, stem from management's theories and assumptions about human beings in general.

If a manager regards his employees as people who inherently dislike work, who will avoid it if given the chance, he tends to set up methods of control designed to coerce the employee into putting forth adequate effort. Instead of achieving this purpose, the development of these control techniques communicates to the employee that he is expected to fall down on the job. The problem for the employee, under these circumstances, is to seek ways to outwit these control devices. Featherbedding, indifference, slowdowns, and the like, are examples of how ingenious the employee can be in defeating the imposed aims of management.

The realities of the situation, as seen by McGregor, are that people obtain real satisfaction in their work and that effort is as natural as play or rest. If a person is ego-involved in the aims and goals of the organization, he will exercise self-direction. The need for imposed external-control devices is then no longer appropriate. Man is potentially a creative and ingenious agent who can become a tremendous asset to his employer if the conditions under which he works are conducive to his development along these lines. The employer and the employee are mutually dependent on each other, the former depends on the employee for productivity while the latter depends on his employer for his livelihood. Subordinates are resources, not errand boys, and should be treated as such. They must become genuine and active partners in decision making and goal setting. Only in this way will the employee be committed to achieving the goals of the organization, for these goals have now become his goals.

Viewed in this light, what effect have administrative practices had on the aide, and what might be done to correct these deficiencies? Basically, most administrators believe that the aide is a person who works in a mental hospital only because he is so technically inept that he cannot get a better paying job elsewhere. The assumption is that the attendant, if he were able to make more money in another line of work, would leave the hospital setting. Those who would not leave are sometimes felt to be emotionally sick people who gain psychological satisfaction in dominating and controlling the lives of patients. If this is an accurate reflection of how a supervisor feels about the aide group, he has no choice but to devise certain control techniques in an effort to force as much work as possible out of his supposedly inept employee. Training courses, inspection rounds, job descriptions, and counseling designed to motivate or threaten the employee, become the traditional techniques of such supervision.

The profound tragedy in this typical attitude is the failure to realize that most aides gain a great deal of satisfaction in their work and that they take pride in what they can accomplish. How else could they tolerate the frustrations of the institution? Some people want to feel needed, and in the mental hospital they find people who desperately need them. Others find a great deal of satisfaction in being part of a social peer group whose members regard them with esteem and respect. Such an aide is unlikely to accept another job in which he would not experience status and recognition from a peer group, even though his salary might be higher. By focusing on the problems of the alcoholic or character-disorder attendant, we professionals have neglected to realize that in every mental hospital there is a core of dedicated people who could be a tremendous asset to us. They are in a position to be of real help to the professional in achieving mutually shared goals because they are just as concerned about the welfare of the patient as are the professional staff, and often more so.

How does one go about providing a situation conducive to the development of the aide as an active partner in the rehabilitation of the patient? Each institution must examine closely both the ways in which it communicates to the aide that he is an esteemed and valuable person and the ways in which it conveys to him that he is a person of little or no real importance. The better attitude in supervision might be for the supervisor to communicate to the aide, in every possible way, that he is a potential asset. The supervisor works with him, not because he needs to be watched and spied upon, but because it is a pleasure and a privilege to do so. In this way, the supervisor creates the expectation for responsible behavior on the part of the aide. In most of our institutions, however, drastic changes in attitudes toward the aide will have to occur before it is possible to create a climate in which the aide feels that he is accepted. Unless this happens, and unless the aide feels respected and supported as an individual in his own right, he will not risk bringing to his work the spontaniety and creativity so often lacking under present circumstances. Responsibility, spontaniety, and creativity are not the contributions of an employee whose role is externally controlled.

In addition to creating the expectation for responsible behavior, the actual situation in which the aide works must provide him with clear-cut rewards for this kind of behavior. In one retraining study, a demonstration ward was established and staffed with a carefully chosen group of aides, nurses, and professional personnel (Vaughn, 1961). Every four months a group of 16 aides were assigned to this special unit. There they observed the training staff interacting with patients. The newly assigned aides found that they too were expected to interact actively with patients. Staff discussion groups, individual counseling, and models of interaction were provided to assist them in accepting their role of active participants. They began to give up well-established patterns of inactivity and control, and instead began to work actively with patients.

At the end of four months, the aides in training were transferred in small groups to other wards, where it was hoped they would continue this active role. Within two or three months, however, they began to relinquish their role as active participants and to return to their former roles of limited patient contact. Rather than regarding this training program as a failure, one must realize that the behavioral patterns of even the older, custodially oriented aides were altered under the particular training conditions. The major failure of the program seemed to lie in expecting that newly acquired behavioral patterns would endure regard-

less of the situation in which the aide later found himself, a situation without rewards for aide-patient interaction.

If one adopts the viewpoint that behavior is a function of the conditions under which it occurs, one is no longer satisfied to label an aide as lazy or irresponsible and to feel one now understands the problem. To do so assumes that behavior occurs *regardless* of the situation, and that the quality of laziness, for example, will endure under all circumstances. Making the assumption that the difficulty lies entirely within the aide suggests that the aide can be changed only by major retraining or removal (Caudill, 1958). One of our finest aides at Fort Meade, who won the "aide of the year" award shortly after being assigned to the research building, is an excellent case in point. On his previous assignment, he was described by his supervisor as unmotivated and uninterested. The supervisor's surprise at his winning the award was no greater than ours when we found that he previously had been regarded as only mediocre. Anyone who seriously hopes to bring about role change must understand the social situation in which people work, for the things people do are largely a function of the situation in which they work. Competent psychiatric leadership, then, is that which fosters and develops the kind of milieu that encourages individuals to make a significant contribution (Bravos, 1965).

Attempts have been made to increase the aide's level of participation or to change his role in relation to patients. Focusing on only one or two aspects of the aide's relationship to patients, most of these attempts did *not* change the conditions under which he worked and were only partially successful in producing measurable differences in patient adjustment (see Appleby, 1963; Freeman et al., 1958; Sines, 1959; and Spohn et al., 1963). When a real attempt is made to involve the aide in *all* aspects of the program the outcome on patient rehabilitation is consistently positive (Galioni et al., 1953; and Lapolla, 1961).

The thesis of this book is that changes in aide behavioral patterns are not likely to persist or to have a significant impact on patients unless there is change in the situational conditions in which the aide works. The aide who acts the role of a disinterested, inactive, and unmotivated person is as much a product of the institutional setting as is the apathetic and withdrawn long-term patient. If the aide is to play the role of an active participant in the patient's rehabilitation, then rewards for playing this role must be built into the actual work situation. Not only must the aide be actively supported in interacting with patients, but information and suggestions that result from his increased patient contact must become the basis for patient rehabilitation planning. The aide must be heard at every decision point (Belnap, 1956). In reality, the mental hospital is perhaps more accurately described as a place where aides work, assisted by doctors and nurses, rather than a place where doctors and nurses work assisted by aides (Hall et al., 1952).

SUMMARY

Using nonprofessional manpower in psychiatric rehabilitation will continue to be a critical problem as long as one assumes that the treatment role should be reserved for those who are professionally trained. Few hospitals have succeeded in utilizing the manpower resource of the psychiatric aide group. The aide, traditionally playing a role of custody and control, seems reluctant to give up this role for one of therapeutic interaction with patients. Such tactics as calling the aide a member of the treatment team, training the aide in formal classroom settings, and increasing the aide staff so there is more time for interaction with patients, have failed to develop this manpower resource.

Analysis of the social setting in which the aide works reveals some of the reasons for the failure to involve the aide as a more active partner in treatment and problem solving. Although the professional staff tell the aide he is an important member of the team, our actions reveal that we do not really believe this. Our techniques of supervision communicate to the aide that we anticipate poor performance, since outstanding performance is usually ignored, while an occasional infraction of a rule warrants considerable attention from supervisors. Interaction with patients typically receives little recognition from the aides' supervisors. The professional staff, who know little about what goes on between the aide and his patient, continue to attribute patient improvement solely or primarily to drugs and psychotherapy.

Even when the professional staff make a sincere effort to involve the aide as an active participant in decision making and treatment, they find him resistant to change. The aide is typically found to identify with his own peer group and to adopt the values of this group rather than the values of the professional staff. He views the latter group with suspicion and hostility. Although the formal organization of the hospital places the responsibility for treatment in the hands of the professional staff, it is often the aide who can make or break a program by determining which procedure he will support and which he will ignore. Remaining uninvolved with the professional staff, the aide experiences considerable job-satisfaction status in his own peer group, as well as control over his own role. Only under those circumstances in which the professional staff is willing to involve the aide as a *genuine* partner of the treatment team is the aide likely to adopt the values of the professional group.

Endorsing many concepts and following many practices of bureaucracy, the mental hospital inhibits the aide from taking an active role in the treatment process. In the bureaucratic structure it is generally assumed that those at the top of the hierarchy can make the best decisions, an assumption which places little value in decision making at lower levels. In the bureaucratic structure, role rigidity is emphasized, and various staff and patient groups are merely expected to comply. Role specialization is encouraged so that everyone knows who is to do what. Viewed as disrupting the orderliness of the bureaucratic operation, role overlap and flexibility are discouraged. On the assumption that standardization of role functions prevents complex situations from becoming chaotic, rules and regulations are substituted for independent decision making. In the bureaucratic structure, also, loyalty to one's service or department is stressed while loyalty to one's ward team or treatment program is viewed as rebellion.

Some progress has been made in granting more authority and control to the ward team by adopting such strategies as the unit system with its decentralization of authority and responsibility. Within the team structure, however, status hierarchy and role rigidity often resemble, in miniature, the larger bureaucratic organization. Typically, the application of team leadership is not one of shared problem solving nor working through others, but rather a continued exercise of power and control. Sharing decision making with all members of the team involves some risks. Some decisions, as, for example, which drug to prescribe for which patient, cannot be shared. The risks involved in shared problem solving, however, are far outweighed by its advantages. A team member, for example, is much more apt to implement a decision that he feels is "our" decision rather than one felt to be "his" (the team leader's) decision. In general, however, team leaders do not value the process of working with and through others, nor have they the training necessary to accomplish this.

Basic changes in attitude regarding the importance of one's co-workers are needed if such co-workers are to become involved, creative, and dedicated partners in the treatment team. The assumptions of the professional staff create the interpersonal situation that communicates to the aide whether he is regarded as lazy and ignorant or important and productive. As a result, our assumptions become self-fulfilling prophesies, for if we believe that the aide is basically inept and unmotivated he will live up to those expectations. The aide's role emerges from, and is a product of, the social and interpersonal situation in which he works.

5

The Structure of the
Experimental Program

What would happen if a program could be developed in which the psychiatric aide really became an active participant in the treatment of the hospitalized schizophrenic? This question was of sufficient interest to the professional and nursing staff of the Veterans Administration Hospital, Fort Meade, South Dakota, so that arrangements were made during 1958 to support a study in which this question could be answered. This 600-bed hospital had six treatment buildings, one for admission and intensive treatment, two for continued treatment of nongeriatric patients, and three for geriatric patients. During the fall of 1958, plans were made to set up one building as an Experimental Unit in which the focus of treatment would be the development of a high level of interaction between the aide and the patient. Two other buildings would serve as Nonexperimental Units, and were free to develop their treatment programs along whatever lines they chose. Fortunately (for this study), no attempt was made to develop an aide-patient interaction program.

Other than the variable of the aide's role, all three programs had many basic similarities. All three used ataractic medication rather frequently, with an average of 65 per cent (experimental) and 62 per cent (nonexperimental) of the patients receiving ataractic medication during 1959, 1960, and 1961. All three buildings used activity assignments, with about two-thirds of the patients scheduled for such areas as Occupational Therapy, Corrective Therapy (sports), Manual Arts, and Recreation, and the other third scheduled for Hospital Industry assignments and outside details. Ordinarily, each patient was scheduled for about six hours of activity per day, with 84 per cent (Experimental Unit) and 73 per cent (Nonexperimental Unit) attendance recorded. On the

Experimental Unit, the psychiatric aides generally accompanied their patients to activities. With all but their most regressed groups, the Non-experimental Units tended to use patient group leaders, who kept a record of attendance.

Each of these buildings held team meetings once a week to consider treatment planning for new admissions and discharge planning for improved patients. In addition to the ward physician, nurse, and aides, these meetings were attended by the psychiatric service chief, a psychologist, a social worker, and an activity therapist (a representative from the physical medicine department). Final decisions regarding the disposition of patients presented for discharge were ordinarily made by the chief of psychiatric service. This tended to insure that the standards for release were fairly constant between the Experimental and Nonexperimental Units.

As will be seen at the end of Chapter 6, all three buildings worked with similar groups of schizophrenic patients. All schizophrenic patients under 65 years of age were evaluated on the basis of (1) length of hospitalization, (2) behavioral adjustment, (3) marital status, and (4) age. At the beginning of the study, 262 male schizophrenic patients resided in the three buildings. One hundred fifty four patients were transferred between buildings so that each building had schizophrenic patient populations with the same proportion of acute and chronic, well adjusted and poorly adjusted, and young and older patients. Each building also received new patients on a strict rotation basis. Between March 1, 1959, and March 1, 1960, an additional 74 schizophrenics were admitted to the buildings in rotation and were included in the project. This resulted in a total of 336 patients in the project, 122 assigned to the Experimental Unit and 214 similar patients assigned to the Non-experimental Units. Nonschizophrenic patients were assigned in rotation to each building but were not evaluated as part of the study.

In each of the three buildings, the schizophrenic patient was followed as a project patient for at least 30 months. If a patient achieved a community release sometime during the 30-month period, he was evaluated regarding his social and work adjustment after 3 consecutive months, and again after 12 consecutive months, in the community. A very high proportion of community follow-up ratings was obtained. For example, the employment status of 100 per cent of those patients achieving 3 and 12 consecutive months in the community was determined. Also, on 97 per cent of these same patients, a rating of their social adjustment was made by someone who had personal contact with them.

FUNCTION AND STRUCTURE
OF THE EXPERIMENTAL UNIT WARDS

At this point, the similarities of the units end. The remainder of this chapter will present the program features of the Experimental Unit that were different from those in the Nonexperimental Units. What had been the Acute and Intensive Treatment Building was designated as the Experimental Unit. This choice was made primarily because the structure of this building was different from that of the other two buildings. The Experimental Unit had three separate wards, each with 35 to 44 beds. The other two buildings, that had 90 to 100 beds each, did not have separate wards. If a patient were too disturbed to be handled in the Nonexperimental Buildings, he was sent to a well-staffed 40-bed maximum-security ward located in another building. Since fewer nursing personnel were needed in the large Nonexperimental Buildings, and since the special rehabilitation program required adequate numbers of aides on the Experimental Unit, the decision was made to select the building which, by its physical structure alone, required more aides. During the 30-month study, the Experimental Unit averaged 6.4 day-shift aides per 100 patients as compared to 4.9 aides per 100 patients on the Nonexperimental Units.

As the patient's behavioral adjustment improved on the three wards of the Experimental Unit, he moved from the closed ward to the open ward, and finally to the discharge ward. As his social skills increased to the point where it was felt that he could handle the level of independent functioning required on the next best ward, he was proposed for transfer. For example, a withdrawn patient on the closed ward would begin to participate in the scheduled activities, to take responsibility for his dress, to communicate more clearly, and so on. At this point the aides would typically propose that he be given a privilege card for the evening hours. Next he would move to the open ward and participate in more complex activity assignments and would receive town passes. As he became skilled in handling these, he was asked to choose an individual Hospital Industry assignment. After demonstrating adequate work and social skills, tentative plans for discharge would be discussed with him.

Once this level had been reached, the patient was transferred to the discharge ward where he was encouraged to carry as much responsibility for his own discharge planning as possible. He wrote his own letters to relatives and/or took town passes to look for work. His progress in this planning was reviewed frequently at the ward team meetings. The aides, psychiatrist, nurse, research psychologist, and industrial therapist reviewed the patient's planning with him. A patient on either the open ward or on the discharge ward who could not meet the expectations of that ward was usually transferred back to the ward from which he had come. On the discharge ward (Ward B), for example, if a patient did not meet the expectation of being actively involved in planning for his discharge, he was transferred back to the open ward (Ward A). If, on the open ward, he did not meet the expectation of going to, and participating in, his activity assignments, he was transferred back to the closed ward (Ward C).

The character of these three wards actually took about 18 months to evolve. Originally there were two locked wards (Ward A and Ward C) and one open ward (Ward B). Within two months, it was decided that the doors of one of the closed wards would be opened (Ward A). Although five beds were reserved on the one remaining locked ward (Ward C) for patients who could not manage this newly opened ward, no incident occurred requiring a transfer to the locked ward. The newly opened ward (Ward A) began to compete with Ward B for privileges, such as number of evening hours, town passes, and cash rather than canteen coupons. Within six months there was so little difference between the two open wards that patients could see no reason to transfer from one open ward to the other.

At this point, one of the aides proposed that Ward B become a discharge ward. Well-adjusted patients who had become comfortably institutionalized on Ward B were exchanged for patients nearing discharge on Ward A. There were several instances in which well-institutionalized patients who had previously developed transient symptoms of psychosis following any discussion of discharge (thereby blocking their discharge), began to request or accept a transfer from Ward A to the discharge ward, Ward B. Many of them subsequently were able to achieve a discharge and remain in the community, in large part because the expectation of both patients and staff was that everyone on Ward B worked toward discharge.

The Ward B patients were allowed to draw increased amounts of money from their own accounts each week. They were given complete freedom to take part in, or refrain from, evening off-ward activities; and they could take day-long passes to look for work in Rapid City, about 35 miles away. The Ward A patients were given less money, and were required to attend certain scheduled evening activities. They were also allowed passes to the nearby town for three hours each Saturday. The problem of "no difference" between Ward A and Ward B was thus largely solved, and the missions of the two became clearly different.

Meanwhile, the closed Ward C patients began to have difficulty making the transition to Ward A. The more withdrawn patients had not yet begun to function at a level high enough to successfully manage the open ward. The Ward C aides felt that they were "scraping the bottom of the barrel" in finding patients able to handle Ward A. Consequently, in the early months of the program, about 50 per cent of all transfers from Ward C to Ward A initially failed and were returned to Ward C. One technique introduced during the transitional phase was to have one aide on Ward A responsible for about 10 borderline patients who had just come from the closed ward. This solution temporarily solved the problem of transition between Ward C and Ward A; eventually it became unnecessary.

By about the eighth month, many of the closed-ward patients had improved to a level where they no longer had trouble making the adjustment to the open ward. During the remainder of the program, there was increasing pressure on Ward A for enough beds to handle patients who had improved enough on the closed ward to warrant transfer to the open ward. Ward C then began to give their own privilege cards to patients waiting for a vacancy on the open ward, if these patients were able to take responsibility for themselves during the evening hours. During October, 1960 (18 months after the beginning of the project), the closed ward, Ward C, had an average patient population of between 18 to 19 patients, as compared to an average population of 38 to 39 patients during the early months of the project. Of these 18 to 19 patients on Ward C, only 6 were not privileged. In general, the higher level of behavioral adjustment of the patients necessitated an upgrading of all three Experimental Unit wards over a period of several months . . . an upgrading stimulated by the patient's increased capacity to handle himself more adequately.

THE ACTIVITY PROGRAM
AND ITS EMPHASIS
ON BEHAVIORAL ADJUSTMENT

The typical patient on the closed ward attended four activity periods each day. From 8:30 to 9:45 A.M., he and his group (accompanied by three to five aides) went to the Occupational Therapy area. From there he went to the Recreation area and participated in pool, cards, and bowling. After lunch he attended Corrective Therapy sessions and took part in such activities as volley ball, shuffle board, etc. Finally, there was a social period on the ward during which the patient played cards and checkers. At all times there were between three and five Ward C aides participating with this group at each activity.

On Ward A, the newly opened ward, most of the patients at first went to activities in a large group. Only a few were assigned to Hospital Industry jobs. This group's first assignment was a period of recreation similar to that on the closed ward, but one that had more variety and range of activities. During the second morning period, patients went to Manual Arts Therapy where they participated in woodworking, printing, lapidary work, and photography. Later, however, Educational Therapy was substituted for Manual Arts Therapy. In this activity, the group discussed world events and educational movies. After lunch they took part in a ward social, often competing for prizes. During the fourth period they engaged in such projects as cement block manufacturing, log peeling, and fence building. The groups on this open ward were accompanied at all activities by one or two aides.

Gradually, as the overall level of patients' behavioral adjustment rose, more and more patients on Ward A were assigned to individual Hospital Industry jobs. Most of those who took Hospital Industry assignments, however, continued coming to Educational Therapy. As patients began to take individual assignments in Hospital Industry, the role of the aide changed. He began to visit each patient in the job setting where he worked. Here he talked with both the patient and his supervisor, and in this way was able to remain personally involved with each of his patients.

The discharge ward, Ward B, had no group activities at any time during the program. All patients were assigned to individual jobs in Hospital Industry, and were expected to keep their own appointments. Much of the informal talk between patients on this ward centered around their success in job seeking and plans to return home. Once each week, these plans were reviewed with the ward staff.

New patients, admitted to the Experimental Building in strict rotation, as has been indicated, were assigned a bed on either Ward A or Ward C, depending on their initial level of behavioral adjustment. Approximately two thirds of all new admissions assigned to the experimental program started on Ward A. Their progress in activity assignments followed the same pattern as that already described for the resident patients.

No additional programs were adopted by the Experimental Building although some were attempted briefly. Patient government was tried on the discharge ward, but was not especially successful, and was discontinued. Small groups on Ward A, led by an aide, nurse, or activity therapist, proved to offer little help beyond that found in the day-to-day contact between patient and aide; these groups were also dropped. Individual psychotherapy was used in only one or two instances. No discharge-planning groups or orientation groups were held, nor was group psychotherapy attempted. Ward meetings (open discussion) were tried briefly, but seemed to add nothing. In short, the entire program was handled with a minimal use of those treatment skills which typically require specialized or professional training.

That none of these additional programs proved to be of value may seem strange to those who have experienced a great deal of success with patient government, small-group discussions, open ward meetings, individual and group psychotherapy, and discharge-planning groups. It was our experience that these approaches seemed artificial in comparison with the spontaniety of the interaction between patients and aides in the activity setting. For example, when small groups were tried with open ward patients, it seemed that we were communicating something like this, "Once each week at this time we will discuss your feelings and problems," as if to say, "What went on between us all the rest of the week doesn't count." Also, these other approaches were primarily verbal, as contrasted to the interaction of the activity areas which focused on the actual behavior of the patient and his feelings in relationship to his behavior. The amount of the behavioral and verbal interaction between patients and staff, as will be seen later, had already increased fourfold before we tried any of these more formalized verbal group approaches. Had we not already had a high level of aide-patient interaction, it may well have been that the addition of some verbally oriented group approaches would have filled a void for patients and staff.

One of the primary reasons the psychiatric aides were able to function effectively within this treatment program was the emphasis on behavioral adjustment. Within the framework of these clearly differentiated wards, the movement of a patient through the building depended on how well he was able to participate in activities, to handle privileges and passes, and to talk with, and respond to, those about him. The aide who worked with a given patient was able to tell the patient exactly what was expected of him in the particular ward setting where the patient found himself.

The aide, moreover, was able to commit himself to the patient and to describe to the patient the consequences of his acts. Within this behavioral adjustment framework the aide could tell the patient exactly what he must do to move on to the next higher level or ward. In this way, the aide became more important to the patient in that he was able to make and keep commitments to him.

In many traditional programs, the aide is often hampered by having to be vague in response to patients' inquiries about ward transfer, privilege cards, or discharge. When the professional staff deny a role of active participation in decision making to the aide, he is unable to relate to the patient in a clear, concise way. If the aide has to suggest to the patient, "You'll have to ask the doctor about that," his own significance in the life of his patient is decreased.

This program, then, could be considered a situation in which both the patient and the aide experienced a well-structured program. In most hospitals, the patient who asks when he can be transferred to an open ward is told, "When you are better," or "When the doctor thinks you are ready." Such vague responses can only serve to heighten the patient's perception of the world as a confused and uncertain place. In this program, however, the patient received constant feedback on the consequences of his acts and was made aware of the perception that others had of him, their reactions to him, and the expectations held for him. Moreover, he interacted with aides who were encouraged to "be themselves" in relating to him. The structure of this program, with its clearly defined levels of expectation, offered a framework in which both aide and patient could participate, a framework which was geared to the modification of behavioral adjustment. Since it was a framework which the aide could grasp easily and participate in effectively, no formal training of the aides was necessary. Encouraged to be genuine and spontaneous, the aide began to use those natural skills he already possessed for interacting with people.

APPROACHES TO MODIFYING
AIDE-PATIENT INTERACTION

The critical task to be faced first in this program was one of increasing significantly the amount of interaction between the schizophrenic patient and the psychiatric aide. During January and February, 1959, time samples of aide-patient interaction in the off-ward activity areas revealed that the aides were spending an average of 86 per cent of their time in such non-patient-contact activities as reading to themselves, watching patients, or talking with other aides. Having escorted the patient group to an activity area, the aide would turn the patients over to the activity therapist and withdraw from further patient contact until the end of the activity period. Although they remained available to assist in controlling the abusive patient or to handle other emergencies, they were largely unavailable to the patient for direct interpersonal interaction with him.

In adopting almost any treatment approach with schizophrenics, the amount of interaction with him becomes one of the critical treatment variables. If one believes, for example, that the schizophrenic lacks adequate social skills, interaction is the vehicle that alters these deficits. If one believes that the schizophrenic is helped most by intruding into his world of withdrawal, hallucinations, and delusions, then intrusion requires interaction. As reported in Chapter 2, we chose to adopt the concept that the primary disorder of schizophrenia is a breakdown of ego boundaries, not because there is any final proof that this is the most adequate theory to explain the schizophrenic disorder, but because this theory offers an excellent rationale for interaction with the schizophrenic patient. The successful therapist, as hypothesized by the ego-boundary theorists, is one who can interact openly and spontaneously and establish a "genuine relatedness" with the patient.

The ego-boundary theory of schizophrenia postulates that the patient must have meaningful contacts with others in order to again learn to separate what is self and what is not-self. As long as this differentiation of ego boundary remains vague, the psychopathology, the disorganization, and the social withdrawal of the schizophrenic patient will continue. Interaction with the patient alters the symptoms of the disorder. As the patient begins to become involved in interaction with others, such symptoms as delusions and hallucinations begin to disappear (Boyd et al., 1954; Ellsworth and Clayton, 1959; and Kellam, 1961). Although Myerson (1939) initially viewed "total push" as modifying only the patient's behavior and not attacking the basic pathology, we view the interaction with the schizophrenic patient as a direct attack on the basic disorder itself, preferring the ego-boundary theory to explain our rationale. The success of the present program, then, depended on increasing significantly the amount of interaction between the psychiatric aide and the schizophrenic patient.

The roots of the aide's inactivity in relation to the schizophrenic patient were found to be complex. Initially, some of the aides expressed the feeling that it was wrong to constantly interact with patients because this might cause the patient to become upset. The aides had typically developed the belief that it was better to leave the patient alone. Certainly it was often better to leave the patient alone if one wished to maintain a quiet ward. But, as suggested earlier, such practices were unlikely to alter the schizophrenic's lack of differentiation between himself and his environment.

The aides also stated that it was the job of the activity therapist to work with the patient. They saw their job as primarily that of making sure the patient was quiet and did not disrupt the ward and activity routine. They felt that they were not paid to do the work of the therapist. As with their first belief, namely, that interaction was often disrupting to the patient, this second opinion arose out of the context of their traditional work setting. Some of the activity therapists, for example, felt that an active aide often interfered with their program. Some felt that if the aide did much of what they did, their job security and status would be threatened. The aide's relative lack of interaction in these activity areas was reinforced by the activity therapist's expectation that the aide should continue to play his traditional role.

Communicating to the aide that interaction with patients was not his primary job, the Nursing Service of Fort Meade Hospital had reinforced a minimal level of aide-patient interaction. Some of the older aides recalled past instances in which they had been reprimanded for wasting time talking to patients. For example, one aide was observed talking to a recently admitted patient. Reported to his supervisor, he was asked what he had talked with the patient about. He replied that he was trying to get to know the patient, where he came from, what he did, and so on. He was told that the hospital employed social workers to talk to patients about these matters and that it was not *his* job to do so. The belief was established, then, that the aide wasted his time in talking with patients, and that he was working *only* when he cleaned the ward, made beds, or escorted patients. After the aide-interaction program began, one supervisor said, "Even now when I see an aide talking to a patient, I have an urge to tell him to get back to work and to *do* something. I know this isn't right, but I've lived with this idea so long I can't change it easily." The aide-interaction program, then, was introduced into a situation that had functioned with a tradition of minimal aide-patient contact.

Before the project began, some of the hospital's professional staff stated that they felt the aide should be more of an active participant in the life of the patient. Still remaining, however, were many nonverbal cues which communicated that few really accepted this in practice. For example, during late 1958 and early 1959, the ward nurse very rarely attended the off-ward activities. As long as the aide did nothing that resulted in a complaint about him, little attention was paid to his off-ward interaction with patients. About the only time an aide's supervisor did talk with him at length was when he had done something wrong. The aide who tried to become active in working with patients received little, if any, increased recognition for his efforts and only enhanced the possibility that someone would complain about him if he did something wrong.

The problem of low aide-patient interaction was assumed to be a function of the conditions under which it occurred. It seemed relatively meaningless to label an aide as "lazy" or "irresponsible," because in doing so, one assumes that such behavior occurs *regardless* of the situation, and that the quality of "laziness" will endure under all circumstances. Throughout the project this writer became convinced that such labelling process was useless in understanding aide (or patient) behavior. For example, an aide was transferred to the Experimental Unit shortly before the program started. On his previous ward, he was considered to be "unmotivated" and "disinterested" in his work. Within the first year, his behavior had changed so markedly *in the situation of the interaction program* that he won the Aide-of-the-Year Award. Another aide, labelled as excessively "aggressive" and "abrupt" with patients at the start of the program, won recognition the following year in the Aide-of-the-Year Award program. In general, even older aides, who had developed consistent patterns of passivity, began to interact with patients *within the situation* of the Experimental Unit. It should be mentioned that prior to the program, there was no preselection of aides, rather, the aide group on a unit before the program began remained on that unit.

It was felt that somehow the aide must find that his work situation offers meaningful rewards for a high level of interaction with patients. The following procedure was used to change the situation in the Experimental Unit to one that was conducive to such a high level of interaction. First, a model for aide-patient interaction was introduced. (See Bandura and Walters, 1963, for a discussion of the importance of this approach to modifying behavior). An enthusiastic, outgoing psychiatric nurse who interacted freely with patients began spending most of her day with the patients and aides in the off-ward activity areas. The research psychologist also began to spend about one third of his time in these areas. Both people were active in talking with patients, helping them with their projects, and participating with them in their activities. We anticipated that the aide would learn that patients did not necessarily become unmanageable when approached, or, if they did, that the disturbance was a temporary one typically followed by an increase in the patient's participation and interaction. One patient, for example, who hallucinated most of the day, was approached frequently by both the nurse and psychologist. Over a period of two to three weeks, he began to decrease his hallucinating behavior, and eventually dropped it entirely. At the same time, he increased his level of meaningful give-and-take interaction with others. Another patient who consistently refused to participate was lifted bodily from his chair by the nurse and research psychologist, and told that he had a choice of *which* activity he wanted, but that he was not free to choose *no* activity at all. This very withdrawn, manneristic patient became more involved in activities and with people, and subsequently began to improve. These events served to illustrate to the aides that interacting with patients was not necessarily upsetting to the patient, but was likely to result in real behavioral improvement.

The second approach to changing the situation, to make it more conducive to a high level of interaction between aides and patients, was the use of an interaction rating scale. The aides had known for some time that the program would involve increased participation on their part. They did not know, however, the nature of this expected participation. An interaction scale was adopted from an earlier study (Ellsworth et al., 1960) and shown to them. They were asked to rate themselves in order to become familiar with the scale items. At first, the aides rated themselves as engaging in a great deal of patient-contact activity. The activity therapists were also asked to periodically rate each aide, and the composite of these ratings was discussed with the aides. At this point, only one aide said that he was unable to change his pattern of inactivity; he requested a transfer from the Experimental Unit. Although he was asked to try it for a while before transferring, he eventually decided to leave the unit. With this single exception, all other aides accepted this interaction-rating feedback, a few remarking wryly, "You sure shrunk our heads." During the last six months of the program, each aide received from the nurse individual feedback about his interaction behavior. She discussed with each aide the therapist's ratings of his interaction. In general, aides became very interested in seeing how much they had increased in their interaction ratings and looked forward to these feedback sessions. These individual feedback sessions were introduced only toward the end of the program, and, as later discussion will show, resulted in a significant increase in the interaction level.

Interaction ratings served another important function. Over a period of time, the activity therapists began to look for, expect, and support aide-patient interaction in their areas. Their conception and expectation of the aide's role began to undergo change, and in many ways the ratings seemed to change the expectation of the activity therapist as much as it helped the aide himself.

At this point, one might wonder if the aides felt coerced into a role of active participation and accepted it reluctantly. When the activity nurse was unable to attend the activity areas, the aides would let her know they had missed her, and showed concern about the possibility of disinterest on her part. Another cue that suggested that the aides were really involved in the project was that only one aide in the Experimental Unit showed an interest in initially transferring from the program.

Later on, when a new psychiatric building was completed in 1960, all hospital aides were asked if they wished to be assigned to the new building. Only on the Experimental Unit were there no volunteers for transfer. During the course of the study, aide turnover was also very low in comparison with other buildings, another indication of the extent to which the aides became involved in, and identified with, the project.

Probably the best source of information about the extent to which the aides became involved in the Experimental Unit program was the informal reports of the aides' wives. On more than one occasion, wives reported that they had seen a real change in their husbands' interest in their jobs. Before the project began, the aide often came home complaining about various aspects of his job. After the project started, however, many of the wives observed and reported a real increase in their husbands' enthusiasm and interest in their work.

A legitimate question to raise is, "What was the nature of the aide's rewards for increased interaction?" To answer this, we need to discuss what happened to the aides' ideas and observation, and the "feel" for the patient that was the product of their increased interaction with him. At this point, it becomes important to discuss the ward team meeting, one of the unusual by-products of this interaction program.

WARD TEAM MEETING INTERACTION IN THE EXPERIMENTAL UNIT

At first, the personnel on each of the three wards in the Experimental Unit participated in a weekly meeting of their own. This meeting was set up along traditional lines, that is, it was attended by supervisors and professional staff in private, away from the patients. These meetings were heavily loaded with professional staff, including not only the ward psychiatrist and the research psychologist, but also the chief of psychiatric service and representatives of the psychology and social work services. The stated agenda of the meeting was to support the aide in his talking about problems, ideas, and suggestions. Like most traditional team meetings, however, a hidden agenda was the preservation of the status hierarchy existing both between and within professional groups as they competed with each other in these meetings (Caudill, 1958). In our initial meetings, the chief of psychiatry talked most and held veto power over all decisions. An observational study of these meetings revealed that the two psychiatrists, two psychologists, and one social worker were involved in an average of 74 per cent of the interaction (talking or being talked to), the patient 22 per cent, the nurse 3 per cent, and the aides and activity therapists .5 per cent each. The staff with the highest status voiced their opinions freely and discussed diagnosis, treatment, medication, and the like. Their domination of the meeting generally communicated to the aide that he was definitely out of the picture insofar as being able to discuss the really important things concerning the hospitalized patient.

Within a few months it became obvious that the higher-status staff were not willing to shift their emphasis and really support and listen to the aide, nurse, or activity therapist. Finally a hospital-aide meeting was held with the professional staff, and the problem of decision making was discussed openly. The physician's argument ran something like this, "You can't practice medicine by majority vote. Since psychiatry is the practice of medicine, the physician must make the decisions. After all, he is the one who must take responsibility for things that go wrong."

These assumptions were questioned. During the meeting it was argued, for instance, that some aspects of the management of a patient's life are indeed the practice of medicine, but that other aspects such as behavior modification and planning for release, are not entirely medical problems. The aide, for example, has a right and an obligation to voice his opinion about such matters since he knows the patient best on a day-to-day basis. It was also emphasized that generally the *aide*, and not the physician, gets the blame when something goes wrong, and that responsibility assumed by the professional staff in theory was often abdicated in practice. Although the team leader may be at a disadvantage in terms of numbers of people potentially able to vote him down, this will rarely happen in the group simply because he is the leader whose opinions are respected. Finally, it was pointed out that the creative potential of the lower-status personnel is developed only when they feel really free to say what they think, with the expectation that their suggestions will be honestly welcomed. The by-product of this, it was pointed out, is likely to be an increase in the aides' enthusiasm and productivity.

The basic problems of the early team meetings were not solved by this discussion. Apparently, the off-ward professional staff were not able to give up their traditional roles and to relinquish control of the meeting. A decision was reached, however. The chief of psychiatric service and the representatives of the psychology and social work services would continue to participate only in the building's Admission and Disposition staff each week. A restructured ward meeting was developed for each of the three wards and attended by all day-shift aides on the ward, the building psychiatrist, the research psychologist, a nurse, and an activity therapist who worked with the patients on that particular ward. The meetings were also moved into the dayroom where all patients could observe and hear the discussion. In the previous ward staff meetings, there was a tendency for irrelevant discussions to develop. After we moved the meetings to the patients' dayrooms, the discussion remained on a problem-solving level.

In the Ward C (locked) and Ward A (open) team meetings, the psychiatric aides took turns preparing the agenda for the meetings. From his own observations, and from discussions with both patients and personnel during the week, the aide would list the problems to be discussed. He would call the patient to the table, outline the problem by interviewing the patient, and state his observations and feelings. The entire group were then free to respond to the presented problem, stating their own observations and feelings. From an open and frank discussion with the patient, a solution or recommendation emerged. Although initially suggested by any member of the group (including the patient), the decisions adopted were by group consensus.

At first the psychiatrist occasionally reversed the recommendations of the team without consulting them, although in the meetings he would tell them that their suggestions were extremely valuable. A conflicting message (verbal versus nonverbal) concerning his attitude about the importance of the aide was evident. For example, in one of the earlier ward team meetings, the members decided it was advisable to restrict a patient who had been repeatedly drinking on pass. In this particular meeting, the psychiatrist was absent. The team told the patient that he would be temporarily restricted from town passes. The patient replied, "What you guys say doesn't mean a darn thing. Wait 'til the doctor comes back, and I'll get him to change all this." The next day the patient did succeed in having the restrictions lifted and told the aide who had conducted that particular meeting, "Like I told you, I got the doctor to go along with me, not with you." When the aide found out that the psychiatrist had written an order to continue town passes he became very upset and seriously considered resigning. In general, the aides picked up these conflicting messages concerning their importance or nonimportance, and as a consequence many of them withdrew temporarily into their traditional role of noninvolvement with their patients.

In the ward team meeting, recommendations were made regarding ward transfers, activity assignments, town passes, medication changes, and discharge planning. Initially the psychiatrist exercised veto power, but as time went on he used it less and less. Eventually, on occasions of his absence, the group was given the authority to make decisions about the problems presented to them. For example, one patient who had just eloped twice, was proposed for transfer from Ward C to Ward A, the open ward. The group felt that the patient would respond very positively by their showing confidence in him. Accordingly, they recommended his transfer and moved him to Ward A. Upon his return the following day, the psychiatrist supported their action. Over a period of time, the ward psychiatrist discovered that the decisions recommended by the group were at least as good as the decisions he would have made. A relationship of mutual trust between the psychiatrist and his ward staff began to develop, eventually leading to his supporting their recommendations. Instead of overriding the team's decisions or later withdrawing support, he began to discuss with the team those few instances in which he felt he had to veto a recommendation. In this way, the day-to-day treatment planning became the responsibility of the entire group.

These meetings evolved into give-and-take discussions among all participants, personnel as well as patients, and were generally characterized by a great deal of spontaneity. Any patient was permitted to approach the group if he had a problem that was not put on the agenda by the aide conducting the meeting. Any team member was also encouraged to bring up problems for discussion, usually after the agenda had been completed. The patient was also encouraged to participate actively in the discussion about him and knew exactly how each member of the group perceived and reacted to his behavior. He learned how each person felt about the decisions affecting him, such as whether or not he was ready for advancement to a more complex individual assignment, a transfer to the discharge ward or to a closed ward.

Utilization of a great deal of traditionally ignored information is another advantage of this type of open team meeting. The aides and activity therapists become intimately familiar with the patient as he responds to a wide variety of situations. They develop a real "feel" for the patient-as-a-person. The professional staff, on the other hand, tend to react to the patient in terms of the diagnostic label or dynamic formulation evolved through interviews, social history, and psychological test results. The aide and activity therapy personnel live in a world of ongoing and current behavior and react to the patient on these terms. The professional staff, in contrast, tend to react to the patient in terms of his label and his past history. Decisions based on information about the patient, as a person who reacts to a situation on a day-to-day basis, combined with relevant information about his psychiatric status, are much more likely to be sound decisions. Conversely, those arrived at without an awareness of both the patient-as-a-person and his psychiatric status are less likely to be effective decisions.

Another advantage of this type of open give-and-take team meeting is that the patient begins to perceive the aide as a meaningful person. Instead of a custodian who is given little support or recognition by the professional staff, the aide comes to be seen by the patient as someone whose ideas and feelings are regarded as important by the professional staff. Under these circumstances, the aide is more likely to become a truly meaningful person in the patient's life. In addition, of course, these team meetings provide the patient with maximum information regarding how others perceive him and what effect his actions have. He, in turn, is encouraged to react to and modify these perceptions.

Between October 30 and November 4, 1961, a visiting state hospital research nurse (Higgins, 1961) observed and interacted with the ward personnel in the Experimental Unit. Her comments on the ward team are presented, in order to reflect the flavor of these meetings as perceived by an outside person:

These meetings are really team affairs. They are presided over by the aides, who made the agenda. Patients are also invited to participate on their own. The meeting's goal concerns the decisions of patient movement through activities, his medication and his physical care. His adjustment to the hospital expectancies are also reviewed.

By and large, the patient's behavior, rather than the personal feelings of a controlling staff member, determines the patient's therapeutic prescription. This is brought about through this team approach which focuses on patient behavior problem solving. This team consists of aides, nurse, activity therapists, and doctor. The attending staff seem patient-concerned and ward-centered, rather than acting as a representative member of the department that employs them. It was impressive to hear how much the aides know about their patients. They really listen to their patients. Their sincere concern in the patient's welfare was demonstrated. Either aide or patient can bring up a problem. The aide usually decides what action would be the best for his patient.

Another unusual (for me) factor of these team meetings was the conditions under which they are held. I have already mentioned that they were conducted by the aides. However, any decision made at such a meeting, and concerning the patient is done in the patient's presence. Most astonishing is that these meetings are held in the patients' lounge, in the audience of the entire ward.

In addition to these ward meetings held in the patients' dayroom, new admissions and patients proposed for discharge were presented weekly to the Admission and Disposition meeting that included professional staff and supervisors who had little or no direct contact with the patient. Test results were reported, social histories presented, and brief psychiatric interviews conducted. Diagnoses were established for newly admitted patients, and final approval for discharge was given for the resident patients. In these Admission and Disposition staffs, as noted previously, the aide and activity therapist played no real part and privately voiced the opinion that the Admission and Disposition meetings "are a complete waste of my time." After initially attending a few of these meetings the aides began to stay away. It was discovered that they felt not much was expected of them, and that they were only asked to provide a bit of information or to find a patient for the group. Finally the head nurse and activity therapist also began withdrawing from the meetings. Since they had already participated actively in the treatment and discharge planning of their patients, they found it difficult to tolerate the inactivity expected of them in these formal meetings, particularly since this was in sharp contrast to their role at the Ward team meetings.

As noted earlier in this section, the higher-status staff were involved in an average of 74 per cent of the interaction of the Admission and Disposition meetings, while the aide was involved in .5 per cent of the interaction. An observational study of the team meetings on Ward C and Ward A three months after the ward team meetings were started (but before the aides began preparing the agenda) revealed the following interaction rates: psychiatrist, psychologist, and social worker 42 per cent, patient 26 per cent, aide 18 per cent, activity therapist 9 per cent, and nurse 5 per cent. During the subsequent months, the professional staff began to act more and more as advisors rather than direct participants in the meetings, and the aides' interaction level rose to a much higher level until they became meetings ". . . presided over by the aides" (ibid.). It should be noted that this level of aide participation in the ward team meetings developed over a period of several months. Since it requires a relearning of roles, this kind of participation does not come about quickly. The aide must learn to become more and more active, and the professional staff must learn to become less active. Neither role change occurs without persistent effort on the part of all.

QUANTITATIVE CHANGES
IN AIDE-PATIENT INTERACTION

Noted previously, the prestudy rating of aide-patient interaction revealed that the aides were spending an average of 86 per cent of their time in activities that did not involve patient contact. Within four months, the effects of the strategies described (i.e., feedback, interaction models, and active participation in decision making) had become apparent. One could walk into the O.T. Clinic, for example, and observe aides talking to and actively working with their patients. The aides also began to talk with the activity therapists about program modifications which they felt would better meet the needs of their patients. As a result of these discussions, new small group projects were started in the O.T. shop. The aides later asked for and got program substitutions in their ward schedules. In general, their concern for and involvement with their patients was shown by an early and marked increase in their level of interaction with their patients.

In Figure 1, the changes in the off-ward interaction levels are presented. Every four to six months the activity therapist rated each aide on the eight-item scale daily for a two-week period (Appendix A). The interaction scores were based on the extent to which the aide: (1) spent time in patient-contact activity; (2) made brief comments; (3) entered into a "give-and-take" conversation with his patients; (4) involved withdrawn patients in conversation and/or activity; (5) stimulated two or more patients to converse with each other; (6) took an active part in activities with patients; (7) promoted group activity; and (8) interacted with a wide variety of patients. The activity therapist also recorded his estimate of the amount of time the aide spent in patient contact. During the 30-month project, eight rating periods were completed in which all activity therapists rated each aide daily for a period of two consecutive weeks. The aides were not aware that these rating periods had occurred until after the general results were discussed with them. The rank-order correlation between the interaction scores for each rating period and the estimated per cent of time spent in patient contact was found to be .97. Since the average amount of time spent in patient contact is both easy to understand as well as representative of the quality of interaction, this data is presented in Figure 1.

Looking at Figure 1, it may be seen that the interaction level showed an immediate increase, rising from 14 per cent to 57 per cent within the first six months. Did the aides interact more frequently because they felt real support from the nurse and research psychologist who participated actively with them, or because of the physical presence of a professional staff member in the activity area? Interested in this question, we studied the interaction ratings for those activity periods when the research psychologist and nurse were absent from the area. This study revealed that the interaction levels remained as high, when the research psychologist and activity nurse were temporarily absent, as they did during those times when one or both of these people were

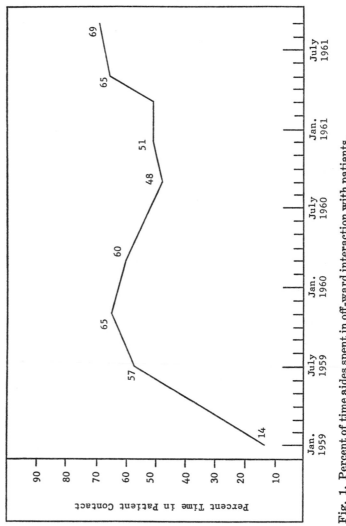

Fig. 1. Percent of time aides spent in off-ward interaction with patients.

present. The aides seemed to be responding to the communication of *interest* demonstrated by the nurse and psychologist as well as to the expectation that their role was to be one of active participation. Communicating this interest and expectation, we found that this interaction did not fluctuate greatly depending on whether or not a professional person was temporarily absent from the activity area.

As can be seen in Figure 1, the average interaction time dropped significantly 16 to 18 months after the project had started. This coincided with the decrease in attendance of the research psychologist in the off-ward activity areas. Also, during this time the first activity nurse left the hospital, and a new activity nurse began accompanying the off-ward groups. At this point in the program the aides would often comment to the research psychologist, "We haven't seen you for a couple of days. Where have you been?" This suggests that the aides were beginning to feel abandoned in the activity areas, an all-too-familiar experience. While it is not necessary for a professional staff member to be present at all off-ward activities, it seems necessary that a sustained interest be communicated to the aide regarding the importance of his role as an active participant. When the aide perceived a sustained drop in interest in a significant staff person, it apparently had an impact on his interaction level.

The new activity nurse was accepted readily by the aides, and their interaction did not decrease further between December, 1960 and March, 1961. The research psychologist, however, accompanied the groups to the activity areas less frequently than he had during the early months of the program. It was decided to try the direct-feedback approach to each aide regarding his own interaction ratings. Previously, the averaged interaction ratings had been presented to the aides after each rating period. Now it was decided that the activity therapists' ratings of each aide would be discussed with him individually.

The new activity nurse started her feedback sessions with each side after the March, 1961 ratings had been completed by the activity therapists. Standard scores were determined for each of the eight interaction performance items. An aide would learn, for example, that the nurse and activity therapists had rated him above average on item 3 (entered into a "give-and-take" conversation with the patients), but below average on item 4 (involved withdrawn patients in conversation and/or activity). The activity nurse would talk with him concerning his perception of his interaction behavior. In general she was very supportive of the aide in these feedback sessions, and the aides became interested in finding out if their interaction behavior had changed by the next rating period. Figure 1 also shows that the average per cent of interaction time rose significantly as revealed by the May, 1961 and the September, 1961 ratings. Our feeling was that these feedback sessions with the individual aide were very useful, and again communicated to the aide that his performance in the off-ward activity areas was important, and that people paid attention to it.

The aides had already discovered they could play an active and effective role in the ward teams only if they knew their patients very well, and that knowing them well required a high level of interaction. During one brief period in the program when the ward team recommendations were being arbitrarily reversed by the psychiatrist, the aides slumped briefly to a very low level of interaction. In spite of encouragement from the head nurse, some of them openly refused to participate. When the professional recognition and support (regarding the aides' importance in participating in decision making) had been withdrawn, there was no longer any direct "payoff" for the aides' sustaining a high level of interaction. For this reason the team meetings, in which the aide becomes a full and active member, were regarded as one of the most important features of this program. It seemed to provide a large part of the motivation for the aide to become active with his patients, getting to know them well, and thereby being able to play a decision-making role in the ward team meetings. Asking the aide to significantly change his interaction level with patients, without reinforcing him for doing so, will not produce sustained change in aides' relationships to patients.

THE QUALITY
OF AIDE-PATIENT INTERACTION

As already noted in the section on therapeutic interaction, the schizophrenic patient seems to profit from interaction with a person who shares his feelings openly in a give-and-take relationship. At first, the aides in this project felt that they might say something "wrong" and that only a person who had had years of training could tell them the "right" thing to say. When the aides would ask, "What should I say to this patient?" the response was, "Say what you feel like saying." Throughout the project the aides were encouraged to be themselves and to do what they felt like doing at the moment in relating to a particular patient. There was some testing of the limits by the aides in order to determine whether or not we really meant what we said. For example, one aide became somewhat abusive in his actions toward a resistive patient. The only comment the activity nurse made was, "I felt the same way," as if to say, "It's okay to be angry." It was often observed that once an aide's feelings of anger toward a patient were openly recognized and freely expressed, the relationship between the aide and patient became one of mutual respect and warmth . . . not, as so aptly stated (Weber, 1947), "without hatred or passion, and hence without affection and enthusiasm." An openness in dealing with one's feelings toward the patient was strongly encouraged . . . not that we endorsed abuse, but neither did we endorse a situation in which no one cared enough for the patient to ever become openly angry with him.

The aides on the Experimental Unit, then, were simply asked to bring to this program the skills which they had already developed, skills of responding to the behavior of others. Most of our aides were married, had raised children, and had established themselves as participating members of the community. They were encouraged to respond to the patient's behavior as they would respond to similar behavior in their everyday contacts with nonhospitalized people. Both patients and aides began to see that their feelings could be expressed openly and honestly. Instead of finding a "double-bind" type of interaction (in which a person experiences the communication of two conflicting feelings) the patient found himself relating to a genuine and real person. The therapeutic value of this genuine aide-patient relationship cannot be overestimated.

The aides were rarely expected to deal directly with such psychopathology as hallucinations or delusions. Instead, they were supported in interrupting this behavior and helping the patient function more effectively in whatever task he was engaged in. When a patient demanded a response to pathological behavior, the aide was encouraged to respond to him as he felt at the moment. A delusional patient who told the aide he owned thousands of acres of land would be told honestly and directly something like, "Come on now, John, don't pull my leg like that." The aides in the Experimental Unit were able to do this, however, without robbing the patient of his dignity. They would rarely argue with the patient about it. Rather they would state their position and then try to respond to the patient in some way to communicate to him that he was still "O.K." as a person. "Let's play a game of pool," would often follow a discussion in which differences of opinion between aide and patient came into the open.

The dignity with which the patients were treated by the aides was observed by the visiting research nurse quoted earlier (Higgins, 1961).

In the four days that I spent in Building 56, I observed an intense and unique type of interaction. Accompanying their patients to each activity, the aides did not assume a role of escort service or guide; rather, they made use of this opportunity to relate and respond to their patients on an individual basis.

In the activity areas, it was interesting to note that the aides often became more involved with the group than the activity therapist. The activities are seen, more or less, as a tool or guide for the aide to interact with the patient. The activity itself does not seem to be as important as the opportunity for the interaction it provides.

It is really impossible to describe what makes this program so successful on a 1–2–3 basis. Rather, it is seen in the sincere warmth and genuine concern these aides have for their patients. It goes much deeper than an aide assisting a patient in sanding a piece of wood that is destined to be the rocker of a rocking horse. It reaches beyond the ward team meeting. This interaction was evident in the accepted attitude the aide holds for his patient during his eight hours of duty. It comes through in many small and spontaneous gestures that I observed, unnoticed, by these aides.

For example, I accompanied a group of patients and aides to some activity, and in this group was Peter. Peter hates leaving the ward. Mr. Hawley, an aide, knows this. He puts his arm around Peter, and through the aide's non-verbal communication, conveys to Peter that the group wants him . . . that this is best for Peter. Or, another example I witnessed in the patients' dining room. A patient who was a feeding problem was given an opportunity to 'eat' without staff interference, such as 'well, well, you are eating today,' (which of course would have brought on the patient's counteracting the staff approval). Instead, the aides supported the patient through silent observation and subtly providing 'seconds.' The patient ate them as well.

Going back and forth from ward to activity, etc. the aides mingle with the patients. They (aides) do not pair off as leaders of a pathetic chain-gang, as witnessed on many hospital grounds. The aides are 'with' the patients. The atmosphere, I felt, was warm and friendly. Patients were accepted as 'buddy to buddy.' No inference of watchman-over-the-patient was portrayed by the aide.

One other feature of this program was that each patient was actively encouraged to participate in the scheduled activities of the Experimental Unit. A withdrawn patient would not be given the choice of withdrawing continuously. Instead, the aides would insist that he enter some activity, and persist until he either participated or at least interacted verbally with them. To allow a withdrawn patient to do nothing but sit continually, in a sense communicates to him that nothing better is expected from him. This often only further reinforces his conception of himself as a worthless person. Insisting that he is capable of participating, on the other hand, communicates to him that the staff feels he is adequate to handle various tasks and personal interactions, and that they care enough about him to insist that he become involved. Challenging the belief that one shows kindness by accepting the patient's wish to withdraw, Forrer (1958) points out that accepting psychotic behavior leads to further regression. The Experimental Unit aides, then, worked actively and insistently toward a goal of maximum participation with their patients.

And finally, this direct approach emphasized to each patient that he was responsible for the consequences of his acts. A patient whose actions resulted in his transfer to Ward C, the closed ward, was always helped to understand that he had brought about his own transfer. It was also made clear to him what he must do to regain privilege status. A patient on Ward A, the open ward, who was not participating in activities would be asked at the meeting about his nonparticipation. Corrective steps he could take, or be helped with, would be discussed with him. A change of assignment, a visit home, a change of medication, and so on, were often suggested and tried, with success. Only when these actions did not work was the patient transferred to Ward C where he could receive more supervision and support. It was always emphasized, however, that the patient himself was responsible for the transfer, and that he alone could determine, by his actions, when he was again ready to move ahead.

In general, the kind of relationship between the aide and patient described above developed largely because the aide received the support necessary for him to become open and honest in his relationship with patients, without robbing them of their dignity. The expectation was made explicit that every patient could and would participate in activities and interpersonal relationships, and that the patient himself was the person responsible for the consequences of his behavior.

Perhaps more subtly, but of no less importance, was the expectancy for change communicated to the patients in their interaction with staff. Initially, both the psychologist and nurse, in their contacts with patients, tended to look for and react to change in the patient. In informal discussions the aides were asked questions about patient change. In turn, aides began to look for, recognize, and react to patient change. Once they became sensitive to these day-to-day changes in patient behavior, they could communicate this to the patient by discussing with him the possibility of his moving to an open ward or taking a more challenging assignment. In this way the expectation of change and improvement began to replace the attitude that most patients are static and unchanging. As will be noted in Chapter 7, the amount of patient change (recorded by the evening aides' ratings of behavioral adjustment) continually reinforced the attitude that change *is* possible with even the regressed, chronically hospitalized patient.

AIDE TRAINING

That classroom training has no measurable impact on aide interaction skills was reported 15 years ago (Hall *et al.*, 1952). New skills in relating to patients can, however, be taught if one becomes involved with aides in the clinical or ward setting. Although we offered no classroom or seminar training for psychiatric aides, their skills in interaction and decision making increased markedly during the program. Undoubtedly this increase in skills stemmed, in part, from the introduction of interaction models (activity nurse and research psychologist) into the activity and ward areas. Also, the aides learned a great deal from each other. In team meetings, an aide would begin to describe an approach he was trying with a particular patient. Other aides not only observed the outcome of his approach, but also felt free to comment on his efforts, to try a similar or different approach. Because of the excellent communication among aides, and between aides and other staff, a great deal of informal training occurred. Formal classroom or seminar training would have communicated to the aides that we believed they did not already possess the skills necessary to become effective therapists and could do so only through training.

An aide-interaction program at the Topeka State Hospital, developed at the same time as the Fort Meade project, illustrates some of the problems that arise when intensive formalized training is introduced (see Colarelli and Siegel, 1966). Both projects were built on the assumption that the therapeutic potential of the psychiatric aide can be increased if 1) the aide becomes spontaneous in his interaction with patients; and 2) the aide becomes actively involved in the decisions concerning patients. The programs differed, however, in that the aides at the Topeka State Hospital were trained in the theory and operation of ego-boundary approaches, psychopathology of schizophrenia, and so on. This formalized training took place almost daily during the four years of the project. For the first three years, the project experienced many difficulties: aide anxiety, a drop in morale, a decrease in the aide-patient interaction, and the unexplained resignation of the nurse. It was not until the fourth year that many of these problems were resolved and the program functioned well.

Few of the difficulties experienced with the Topeka State project became problems in the Fort Meade program. The intensive training given the aides at Topeka State Hospital not only did not seem to solve problems, but may actually have created uncertainty and lack of confidence in the aide. Although aides were told that spontaneity and openness were the essential ingredients of a therapeutic relationship, one suspects that the Topeka Hospital staff also communicated to aides that their effectiveness could be enhanced only when they understood and adopted the complex theoretical system valued by the staff. The Topeka State Hospital program did indeed succeed in rehabilitating a substantial proportion of chronically hospitalized schizophrenic patients, thus illustrating the therapeutic potential of the psychiatric aide. It did so, however, with a great expenditure of professional staff involvement in training, an expenditure that probably created many more problems than necessary or desirable.

Formalized classroom training for psychiatric aides, in our experience, would have been both undesirable and unnecessary for developing effective interaction skills. The effectiveness of our aides' interaction skills was enhanced in the clinical setting through other techniques such as: a) clearly communicated role expectations, b) feedback on role performance, c) the availability of role models, and d) meaningful rewards such as increased status and decision making. Under these conditions, classroom training seemed superfluous at best.

SUMMARY

In order to study the impact of a change in the aide's role on patient rehabilitation, the experimental and nonexperimental programs should be essentially similar to each other in all aspects *except* the aide role. In most respects, the programs were found to be similar (i.e., the use of medication, the use of activity therapy, the process of reaching the decision to discharge, the staffing patterns, the assignments of new admissions, and the similarity of patient characteristics). Other aspects of the experimental program were different from those of the nonexperimental wards, however (i.e., the size of the ward units, the aide staffing ratios, and the availability of the activity nurse and research psychologist for interaction with patients). The Experimental Building had three progressively differentiated wards: a closed ward, an open ward, and a discharge ward. This clear differentiation helped in modifying the patients' behavioral adjustment, for the expectations of each were clear. Special programs such as patient government and small-group meetings were tried but dropped, since they seemed to add little beyond what the aides were already accomplishing in their interaction with patients.

The approaches used to modify aide-patient interaction are discussed in this chapter. Also discussed is the rationale that explains why a high level of interaction was thought to be so important in the rehabilitation of schizophrenic patients. The development of the aide as an active participant in the decision-making process is also discussed. This decision-making role is regarded as essential in sustaining a high level of aide-patient interaction, since the aide must receive recognition, support, and reinforcement for his interaction with patients. The aides did not sustain a high level of interaction with patients when they were not able to put to use their observations and increased knowledge about patients. Participation in decision making allowed the aide to utilize the products of his increased interaction. In order to alter the aide's role, it was necessary to alter the social conditions under which the aide worked (i.e., the recognition and support he received, his participation in decision making, the role of other staff in relationship to him, and so on).

The quantity of aide-patient interaction was found to rise sharply when the situation in which the aide worked was altered. As the social situation changed during the project, there were some fluctuations in aide-patient interaction level. The probable antecedents of this fluctuation are discussed. The quality of aide-patient interaction also changed. The aide was encouraged in his relationship to his patients to say and do what he really felt like saying and doing. Spontaneity, openness, and warmth developed, as noted by a visiting nurse whose observations were also reported in this chapter. Also characteristic of the aide-patient relationship was the aide's ability to confront the patient regarding his sick behavior, for the aides had come to expect, and find, changes in their patients.

PART TWO

The Impact of the Program on Patient Rehabilitation

6

The Research Design

THE EXPERIMENTAL VARIABLE *
—THE AIDE ROLE

Underlying this research is the assumption that the experimental program will be effective in the rehabilitation of the schizophrenic patient only to the extent that the psychiatric aide becomes an active participant in the rehabilitation process. The intent of this study is to evaluate the effects of increased aide-patient interaction (presented in Figure 1, Chapter 5), and of increased aide participation in decision making on the subsequent adjustment of hospitalized schizophrenics. As pointed out at the end of Chapter 4, studies which manipulate one variable at a time may be easier to do and simpler to interpret but they are less likely to significantly affect the rehabilitation outcome. The primary experimental variable of this study, then, was a *general* modification of the aide's role, including increasing his participation in all phases of the program, creating an expectancy for patient change, increasing the aides' significance in the patients' eyes, encouraging the aide to interact with patients in the way he really felt, and providing a framework of behavioral modification rather than a treatment model requiring professional skills. Such a generalized role change makes it impossible to determine which of these ingredients, alone, or in combination, accounted for the subsequent success of the program. It seems to this writer, on the other hand, that many narrowly controlled studies are so superficial that the likelihood of finding any significant results is small indeed. The creation of a truly meaningful role for the psychiatric aide, accordingly, involves the changing of several program ingredients re-

* Those who are unfamiliar with statistics, graphs, and tables may want to read only the summary sections of Chapter 6, 7, and 8. Chapter 9, however, can and should be read by everyone interested in utilizing professionally untrained personnel.

lating to or underlying the development of a significant role for the psychiatric aide.

The primary role of the research psychologist and activity nurse was that of staff development. One cannot expect the aide to interact more with patients without rewards for increased interaction, or to participate more in team meetings without changing the nature of the traditional staff hierarchy in these meetings, nor to try a new and different role unless there is a great deal of support for his doing so. The development of a basic change in the psychiatric aide's role was dependent on the role changes of the psychiatrist, the activity therapist, the activity nurse, and the research psychologist.

It is possible that a second major variable of the experimental program was the interaction of the activity nurse and/or psychologist with patients. It is unlikely that this could have been the *major* variable, however. Several months before the end of the study the research psychologist, for example, decreased the frequency with which he attended the off-ward activity areas. The original activity nurse was replaced by another nurse half-way through the study. This is not to say that the interaction of the nurse and psychologist with patients had no impact on the behavioral adjustment changes or release of patients. It was recently found (Dreiblatt and Weatherley, 1965) that a regimen involving a series of brief, informal 5- or 10-minute conversations between a psychologist and newly admitted patient over a two-week period had a significant impact on changes in the patient's self-esteem, his reported symptoms, anxiety, and the length of his hospitalization. These authors found that informal conversations in which any discussion of symptoms was avoided, had a greater positive effect than symptom-oriented discussions. This type of ego-enhancing, supportive interaction communicates to the patient that he is accepted as a person. Symptom-oriented interaction, on the other hand, is more likely to communicate to the patient that he is socially deviant, inferior, and that he occupies the lowest position in the hospital, with little power and few prerogatives. In the present study, the avoidance of symptom discussion was characteristic of both aide-patient interaction and of the interaction of the nurse and psychologist with patients.

Dreiblatt and Weatherley (*ibid.*) discuss a second important characteristic that underlies the extent to which interaction with the patient becomes meaningful, namely the status of the interactor. They conclude (p. 519):

It is suggested that the status of the contactor may have an important bearing on the efficacy of brief contacts. A message of acceptance from one whom the patient sees as having power and prestige in the social organization is likely to be a more important determinant of the patients' self-perception than a similar message from one of relatively low status. Hence, it should not be automatically inferred from the present data that a program of brief contacts by ward aides or student nurses will have the beneficial effects on patients that were shown here.

Probably the effectiveness of our program would have been severely restricted had we not succeeded in raising the status of the psychiatric aide in the patients' eyes. Conducting the ward meetings in the patients' dayroom and involving the aide as an active participant was designed to raise the aides' status. Also, the patient found the aide able to make a valid commitment to him regarding the outcome of his actions, demonstrating to the patient that the aide was indeed a potentially significant person in his life. These features of the program greatly enhanced the meaningfulness of the interaction between the aide and patient. Without these program features, the status of the aide in the patient's eyes, and therefore the meaningfulness of the interaction with him, would have been no different from that found in traditional programs.

DATA ON MODIFICATION
OF THE EXPERIMENTAL VARIABLE

Our success in raising the interaction level between aide and patient in the experimental program has already been discussed in Chapter 5. Periodic off-ward interaction ratings of nonexperimental program aides with their closed ward patients revealed that their level of interaction remained essentially unchanged during the course of the study (i.e., varying between 16 and 28 per cent). Furthermore, aides in the non-experimental programs rarely accompanied their open-ward patients to activities. Instead, they designated another patient to assume responsibility for seeing that the group got to their scheduled activities.

In team meetings on the nonexperimental wards, time-sample observations revealed that the aides interacted less than 1 per cent of the time, while the professional staff were involved in 82 per cent of the interaction, the patient 13 per cent, and the nurse and activity therapist 2 per cent each. In contrast, in the experimental program meetings held in the patients' dayroom, the aides interacted 18 per cent, the professional staff 42 per cent, the patient 26 per cent, the activity therapist 9 per cent, and the nurse 5 per cent. This represents a significant difference in the degree to which the experimental-program aides took an active part in their team meetings, as contrasted to the participation of their nonexperimental counterparts.

During the summer of 1960, Team Satisfaction Questionnaires were administered to the teams of the Experimental and Nonexperimental Units (See Appendix B). Statistically significant differences were found between the responses of those attending the nonexperimental ward teams, in contrast to those attending the experimental ward teams. On 8 questions, out of a total of 21, the responses of the experimental and of the nonexperimental team members were significantly different beyond the .05 level of confidence. The items that the nonexperimental team members endorsed more often than their experimental counterparts are listed in their order of differences. The nonexperimental team reported significantly more often that (a) their team meetings could be improved a lot (Question 9); (b) they spent too much time accomplishing too little (Question 1); (c) they learned little that helped them deal with patients in general (Question 20); (d) their team meetings were a waste of time (Question 5); (e) people did not really want to hear what they had to say (Question 7); (f) they learned little about dealing with particular patients (Question 21); (g) the decisions were those which the doctors had in mind in the first place (Question 6); and (h) they didn't say anything because they felt they didn't know the patients well enough (Question 12).

The manipulation of the experimental variable, i.e., the aide role, involved several changes. The experimental aide changed and became significantly different from his nonexperimental counterpart in (a) the amount of aide-patient interaction, and (b) the development of the aide as a full member of the team, including his active participation in team meetings and his reported level of satisfaction with the team process. In addition, there was an upgrading of the experimental aides' status in the eyes of the patient, who found that what the aide said really counted. We have shown that the professional staff can play their most effective role by creating a social situation in which the aide can become more effective. This can be accomplished only if the professional staff are willing to break down the traditional status hierarchy in exchange for an honest sharing with the psychiatric aide of treatment responsibility (and related status).

PROBLEMS IN MEASURING PROGRAM EFFECTIVENESS

In selecting various measures of treatment effectiveness, one is faced with a complex task. Discharge or turnover rates have serious limitations. A 500-bed hospital, for example, that releases 250 patients per year, has a 50 per cent turnover rate. This figure tells one very little about the average length of stay, let alone the return rate. For example, Hospital A may have 400 of its 500 beds "frozen" by patients unable to leave the hospital. With 100 actual operating beds, it moves two and one-half patients per year through these 100 beds to achieve 250 releases per year. Hospital B may have only 300 of its 500 beds "frozen," with 200 beds free to receive and release patients. When it releases 250 patients per year, it moves little more than one patient per year through its free beds. Thus Hospital A is more efficient than Hospital B, for the median length of stay for newly admitted patients is about 5 months in Hospital A and 10 months in Hospital B. Both hospitals, however, can report a 50 per cent turnover or discharge rate.

The use of turnover and discharge rates also implies that the hospitals being compared treat the same kind of patients. This implicit assumption is rarely met. Hospitals in large cities often admit a large number of alcoholic patients whose hospital stay is relatively short. For that matter, if such a hospital wishes to increase its turnover or discharge rate, it can do so simply by liberalizing its policy regarding the admission of alcoholics. Hospitals located in rural areas, on the other hand, are often used as a resource for those patients who have failed to respond to treatment in an acute ward of a metropolitan hospital. Because of the differences in types of patients admitted to a metropolitan hospital, the turnover or discharge rate of such a hospital cannot be compared with that of an isolated rural hospital.

And finally, the turnover and discharge statistics typically used by most psychiatric hospitals do not take into account the return rate (rate of community failure) of its released patients. Furthermore, such data as adequacy of community functioning are generally not known to a hospital. One hospital may discharge patients who typically remain emotionally and financially dependent over a prolonged period of time. Another hospital may retain its patients longer (less efficient), but prepare significantly more of them to live independently (more effective).

One technique that offers a better analysis of patient movement than either turnover or discharge rate is the cohort analysis proposed by Kramer, et al. (1955). For example, all first-admission schizophrenic patients who enter a particular hospital are defined as an admission cohort. Hospital A may release 50 per cent of this specified admission cohort in three months, 75 per cent by six months, and 90 per cent within a year from the time of admission. Hospital B may release 40 per cent of a similarly defined cohort within three months, 60 per cent within six months, and 75 per cent within a year of admission. Assuming that the return rate and level of community adjustment is the same for Hospital A and Hospital B (an assumption which is not part of the cohort analysis), Hospital A is clearly more efficient but not more effective than Hospital B with first admission schizophrenics.

An extension of the release-by-time cohort analysis has been proposed by Gurel (1966). He has evaluated the relationship of various statistics to total time spent in the hospital over a four-year period, including readmission time. The admission cohort consisted of 1,274 nongeriatric male veterans who were diagnosed as functionally psychotic upon admission. The patients were followed continuously from the time of their admission until four years later. Subsequent rehospitalization time in both veteran and nonveteran hospitals during this four-year period was recorded for each patient.

The method proposed by Gurel (*ibid.*) to measure treatment outcome was the total number of In-Community-Days (ICD) each patient achieved during this four-year period. One drawback of this method is that it requires a period of four years before data can be reported. Delay of feedback information to the institution regarding its treatment outcome is not satisfactory, since most hospitals are continuously undergoing change in their programs. By the time the four year In-Community-Days are recorded for each patient in the admission cohort, the hospital programs have probably changed.

Gurel (*ibid.*) further reports another approach, data on which can be obtained more quickly, and which correlates .79 with total In-Community-Days over a four-year period. This is the length of hospital stay before the patient is able to achieve a release followed by 90 consecutive days in the community, defined as a "First Significant Release" (FSR). Not only did he find this highly significant correlation (N = 1,250 patients), but also that the rank order relationship of hospitals on FSR-90 and ICD 4 years was .92. Hence, the more readily obtainable number of hospital days prior to a First Significant Release is highly related to total In-Community-Days.

Finding this high relationship between ICD and FSR is perhaps not too surprising in retrospect. In general, a functionally psychotic admission patient often returns to the hospital within 90 days of release if he left before he was prepared to cope with the demands of his community environment. Those who fail in the community thus accumulate additional hospital treatment days until they are able to remain out of the hospital for 90 consecutive days. The FSR-90 figure takes into account, indirectly, many of the readmission data lost by such statistics as release and turnover rates.

By combining the cohort (Kramer et al., 1955) and the FSR-90 approach (Gurel, 1966), meaningful release data for a group of first-admission schizophrenics can be recorded. Hospital A may report that

40 per cent of its cohort obtained an FSR-90 after two months of cumulative hospital time, and that 90 per cent of its cohort obtained an FSR-90 after 12 months of hospital treatment time. Hospital B may report 25 per cent of its cohort achieving an FSR-90 by two-months treatment time, and 65 per cent by 12 months. Assuming that the level of community adjustment is similar for those achieving an FSR-90 from Hospital A and Hospital B, then Hospital A is clearly more effective in treating its patients than Hospital B. This kind of significant release cohort data could also be used for reporting the movement into the community of long-term chronically hospitalized patients. For that matter, one could set his criterion for a significant community stay at 12 consecutive months in the community, rather than 90 consecutive days. At any rate, it appears advisable to report a variety of release criteria in order to provide a comprehensive picture of patient movement into the community.

PROBLEMS IN MEASURING
COMMUNITY ADJUSTMENT

Measures of adequacy of community adjustment following a release from the hospital are essential if one is to evaluate differences in treatment programs. A hospital discharge followed by a prolonged period in the community does not necessarily mean that the patient is functioning adequately. He may, for example, have been placed in a foster or nursing home where he is fed and cared for, a setting that often tolerates deviant behavior but demands little of the patient. Or he may have returned to his family but continued to function marginally in the community.

Perhaps the most extensive follow-up of discharged patients is the study by Freeman and Simmons (1963) who interviewed the relatives of 698 discharged patients. Of these, 49 (7 per cent) either refused to participate, terminated the interview, or were unable to respond adequately. The high proportion of successful follow-ups was achieved by paying professional workers $10 per interview plus travel time and mileage, a cost which would discourage the routine use of this procedure for most hospitals.

In another study (Berger et al., 1964), a less expensive follow-up procedure was used. An extensive questionnaire measuring social, work, and self-care behavior was mailed to relatives and/or friends whom the patient identified at the time of admission as able to provide information. Seventy-seven per cent of the questionnaires were adequately completed and returned following the initial contact by mail, and 84 per cent had been returned after the second mail contact. Thus, 16 per cent of the mail contacts did not result in usable questionnaires, compared with a 7 per cent loss of information in the Freeman and Simmons study (1963). In another study, Fairweather *et al.*, (1960), a return rate of 90 per cent of mailed questionnaires is reported.

With regard to the problem of reliability of community adjustment ratings, Berger *et al.* (1964) report that 64 per cent of the responses from two independent raters were answered identically, while 23 per cent of the answers were only one point apart. No validity data were reported for any of the three questionnaires cited in the last paragraph. It would appear, however, that the reliability of the mailed questionnaires is generally satisfactory. Certainly the mailed questionnaire has the added value of minimal cost as compared with the personal follow-up method. Unless one wanted data of a highly technical nature, such as that gathered by Freeman and Simmons (1963), the mailed questionnaire appears to be adequate for most follow-up purposes.

SELECTING AND EQUATING PATIENT GROUPS

A most unusual feature of the Fort Meade Program is that the schizophrenics who entered the project were not a selected group. They represented open- and closed-ward chronic and acute patients. At the Fort Meade Hospital there were six treatment buildings. An Acute and Intensive Treatment Unit with 70 per cent of the patients nonprivileged, two locked Continuous Treatment Units, and three Geriatric Units. Since the study was limited to nongeriatric (under 65 years of age) schizophrenic veterans, *all* patients who met these criteria from the first three buildings were included in the study. Most large-scale rehabilitation studies that focus on patient-release rates select patients who are able to handle an open-ward situation at the beginning of the study (Fairweather *et al.*, 1960; Fairweather, 1964; Galioni *et al.*, 1953; Howard, 1960; Lapolla, 1961; Miller, 1954; and Stringham, 1952). On the other hand, studies reporting the results of special programs with regressed closed-ward patients usually focus on the "in hospital" improvement of such patients, and rarely report release rates (Kamman *et al.*, 1954; Shatin, 1957; and Sines *et al.*, 1952).

If an investigator has no more than 6 to 12 months to evaluate a program, he apparently has the choice of setting minimal criteria of "in-hospital" improvement for regressed closed-ward patients, or selecting open-ward patients who have already achieved some level of adequate adjustment within the hospital and for whom the prospect of early release is relatively good. This writer previously followed a group of chronically hospitalized, initially closed-ward patients, for a period of four years (Ellsworth et al., 1958). At the end of this period, 49 per cent were in the community. The writer is convinced that an effective rehabilitation program is capable of bringing large numbers of regressed closed-ward patients to open-ward status and subsequent release. These results, however, are not achieved within a short period of time and cannot be evaluated in a 6- to 12-months period.

Each patient in the Fort Meade study was followed for at least 30 consecutive months. If he was discharged during this time, he was followed for an additional 12 months. A total of 336 schizophrenic patients were included in the study, 262 of them hospitalized at the time the study began, and an additional 74 schizophrenics admitted to either the Experimental or Nonexperimental Units during the 12-month intake period. During the 30 months of the project, nine patients died. The numbers of acute, semi-chronic, and chronic schizophrenics are presented for the Experimental and Nonexperimental Units (Table 1).

At the beginning of the study, relevant clinical and background data were gathered on each of the 262 hospitalized schizophrenic residents. A mass transfer of patients was arranged between the three psychiatric treatment buildings in order to equate for: (1) length of hospitalization, (2) level of behavioral adjustment, (3) age, and (4) marital status. Each building, then, had the same proportions of schizophrenic patients who were young and old, well-adjusted and poorly-adjusted, recently hospitalized and continuously hospitalized, and single and once-married patients. These variables were selected for matching experimental and nonexperimental patient populations since other studies have reported them to be related to the probability of release. In the following pages, each of these variables is examined with regard to its relationship to treatment outcome.

The demographic and clinical characteristics used for equating groups of patients should be related to the outcome criteria selected for the evaluation of programs under study. If one is interested in whether or not an experimental program is more effective than a nonexperimental program in returning patients to the community, then the patient populations under study should be equated on those variables related to probability of release. If the patient populations are not equated on prognostically relevant variables, there can be no certainty whether differences in patient characteristics or differences in programs

Table 1 - Number of Experimental and Nonexperimental Schizophrenics Completing 30-Month Study

	Experimental Condition				Nonexperimental Condition			
	Group I*	Group II**	Group III***	Total	Group I*	Group II**	Group III***	Total
Entering Project	38	31	53	122	66	59	89	214
Died During Project	1	2	0	3	1	3	2	6
Completing Project	37	29	53	119	65	56	87	208
Percent of Combined Groups I, II, and III Completing Project Under Experimental and Nonexperimental Conditions	31%	24%	45%	100%	31%	27%	42%	100%

*Group I Schizophrenics = acute patients, hospitalized fewer than two of the preceding five years.

**Group II Schizophrenics = semi-chronic patients, hospitalized between two and five of the preceding five years.

***Group III Schizophrenics = chronic patients, hospitalized all of the last five years.

account for the differences in outcome. Since one of the buildings at the Fort Meade Hospital already contained large numbers of recently hospitalized schizophrenics, the equating of patient populations between buildings became a crucial first step. Of the presumed relevant variables selected for equating the building populations, data presented later on in this chapter revealed that only age was unrelated to outcome. One additional variable that later appeared to be related to outcome was the incidence of lobotomy.

The patients most recently admitted to the Acute Intensive Treatment building were first randomly assigned to the three buildings taking part in the study. The entire schizophrenic patient population was then coded on age, length of hospitalization, behavioral adjustment, and marital status. The overall proportions falling within each category were computed. If one building needed, for example, three married schizophrenic patients between the ages of 35 and 44, hospitalized two to five years, whose behavioral adjustment fell within the 10th and 33rd percentile, the names of all patients in the other two buildings who met these criteria were put in a box. Three names were then randomly drawn and the patients were assigned to the building that needed them. This procedure was followed until the patient groups in the Experimental and Nonexperimental Buildings were equated on the four selection variables.

LENGTH OF HOSPITALIZATION. Brown (1960) recently reviewed 16 studies of the release rates for schizophrenics. He included surveys of the Warren State Hospital, Delaware State Hospital, and New York State Hospital system. The familiar finding that the release curve accelerates rapidly during the first year after admission, and becomes practically flat between the second and fifth post-admission years, was consistently demonstrated. Patients hospitalized beyond two years, for example, had a 6 to 7 per cent expectancy for release. Thus, length of hospitalization is perhaps the first variable which must be considered with equating patient populations.

This finding was verified by the present study. For the 336 schizophrenic patients who entered the project, the probability of release during the first year was found to be highly related to their length of hospitalization. The probability of release within 12 months was between 75 to 80 per cent for patients hospitalized less than two years during the preceding five years (see Table 2). The probability of release within 12 months for patients hospitalized between two and five years was 35 to 47 per cent. Finally, for patients who had spent no time in the community during the immediately preceding five years, 14 per cent were released during the 12 months after their admission to the project. It seems

Table 2 - Release Rates of 336 Schizophrenics* Included in the Project

Amount of time spent in hospital during last 5 years	N	Percent Released Within					
		2 mo	4 mo	6 mo	8 mo	10 mo	12 mo
Between 0 and 1 year	74	27%	55%	65%	70%	77%	80%
Between 1 and 2 years	30	25%	53%	63%	69%	72%	75%
Between 2 and 3 years	30	17%	27%	37%	40%	47%	47%
Between 3 and 4 years	17	12%	18%	18%	41%	41%	47%
Between 4 and 5 years	43	9%	16%	23%	28%	35%	35%
Continuously hospitalized	142	3%	8%	10%	11%	13%	14%.

* Including nine patients who died while on project.

clear from Table 2, that there were three groups of schizophrenic patients who differ on the basis of probability of release. In reporting the results of the experimental and nonexperimental treatment programs, each of the three groups will therefore be discussed separately. Those schizo-phrenics who were hospitalized between zero and two years during the preceding five years will be designated as Group I Schizophrenics. The semi-chronic patients (hospitalized between two and five years) will be designated as Group II Schizophrenics. Finally, those chronic patients continuously hospitalized for five-plus years will be designated as Group III Schizophrenics.

The chronicity of Group I, Group II, and Group III Schizophrenics is not the only characteristic on which these patients differ (see Table 3). Group I and Group II patients were found to be significantly higher in behavioral-adjustment level than Group III patients. Also, significantly fewer of the Group II and Group III patients had ever been married. Finally, both the age and incidence of lobotomy (the latter subsequently found to be related to outcome) were higher for Group III patients than for Group I and Group II patients. In general, the chronic schizophrenic patient (Group III) showed more behavioral regression, was five to eight years older, and had a greater chance of having had a lobotomy

Table 3 - Differences in Characteristics
of Group I, Group II and Group III Schizophrenics

	Group I N = 104	Group II N = 90	Group III N = 142
Time spent in NP hospital during past 5 years	8.4 months (14%)	45.1 months* (75%)	11.9 years** (total time)
Initial Behavioral Adjustment Rating (MACC Scale, Form II)	60 Percentile	54 Percentile	37 Percentile**
Percent never married	60%	77%*	87%*
Age	36.4 years	39.2 years	44.5 years**
Percent Lobotomized	1%	7%	31%**
Percent who were hospital Residents at start of project	40%	87%*	100%**

* Significantly different from Group I (beyond .01 level).

** Significantly different from Group I and Group II (beyond .01 level).

than either Group I or Group II patients. Group I and Group II patients were roughly similar to each other with respect to age and behavioral-adjustment level, although fewer of the Group II patients had ever been married. In addition to the relationship between chronicity and probability of release, some of the variables mentioned above were also found to be related to subsequent hospital release.

BEHAVIORAL ADJUSTMENT. MACC Behavioral Adjustment Scale, Form II (Ellsworth, 1962), was used throughout the study to evaluate the behavioral changes of the experimental and nonexperimental groups. This scale measures four areas of adjustment: mood, cooperation, communication, and social contact. In general, a patient who scores in the upper range (75 to 80) is pleasant and easy to get along with (mood); does what is asked and completes assigned tasks (cooperation); talks realistically and grasps what is told him (communication); and "socializes" well (social contact). A patient who scores in the lower range (16 to 40) adjusts poorly in these areas. The scale was rated by the evening shift aides prior to and throughout most of the study period.

Behavioral adjustment scores have been found to be related to a wide range of other indices of adjustment. In the original work with the MACC Behavioral Adjustment Scale (Ellsworth, 1957) the Total Adjustment Score (Form I) correlated −.69 with independent ratings of psychopathology. The behavioral ratings, obtained upon admission to the hospital, correlated −.41 with length of hospital stay. Finally, the behavioral ratings at time of release correlated −.47 with independent social-worker ratings of community maladjustment. Thus, a patient with a high behavioral adjustment score at the time of admission could be expected to remain in the hospital a *shorter* period of time and show *less* psychopathology than a patient with a low behavioral adjustment score. Upon discharge, the patient with a high behavioral adjustment rating would be less likely to show signs of community maladjustment with regard to his functioning in the areas of family relationships, social relationships, handling of funds, and occupational adjustment.

In the present study, the variables of chronicity (amount of hospitalization), initial behavioral adjustment scores, marital status, lobotomy, and age were analyzed with regard to their relationship to hospital release and community stay. Each of the 336 patients in the present study were placed into two categories for the purpose of this analysis: (1) those who achieved a *significant* release (a release followed by at least three *consecutive* months in the community), and (2) those who did not achieve a significant release during the 30 months of the research project. Phi coefficients of correlations between significant release and (1) chronicity, (2) behavioral adjustment, (3) marital status, (4) age, and (5) incidence of lobotomy, are presented in Table 4.

Table 4 shows the variables of chronicity and behavioral adjustment are most highly related to significant release (i.e., a release followed by three consecutive months in the community). Marital status, history of previous lobotomy, and age were less predictive of outcome.

It is of considerable interest to note that the experimental and non-experimental programs differ with respect to the variables which are differentially related to outcome. The best predictor of outcome for patients in the nonexperimental program was chronicity, whereas the best predictor for the experimental-program patients was behavioral adjustment level. As will be recalled, the Experimental Building patient moved from the closed ward to the open and discharge ward depending on the adequacy of his behavioral adjustment. Once on the discharge

Table 4 - Phi Coefficients[1] of Relationship of Outcome with Chronicity,
Behavioral Adjustment, Marital Status, Lobotomy, and Age

	Total Population N = 336	Nonexperimental Program Patients N = 214	Experimental Program Patients N = 122
Chronicity	.35**	.44**	.21*
Behavioral Adjustment	.34**	.28**	.46**
Marital Status	.13*	.11	.14
Lobotomy	.17**	.19**	.16
Age	.10	.09	.11

* Significant beyond the .05 level of confidence.
** Significant beyond the .01 level of confidence.

[1] Note: In order to compute phi coefficients the variables of chronicity,

behavioral adjustment, marital status, lobotomy, and age were

categorized as follows: hospitalized only part of the last five

years versus all of the last five years (chronicity); MACC score

above 60 versus below 60 (behavioral adjustment); once married

versus never married (marital status); not lobotomized versus

lobotomized (lobotomy); and below 40 versus above 40 (age).

ward, the patient found himself living in a "climate" of preparation for
discharge, a process in which he was expected to participate. Recall also
that the program of the Experimental Building was designed to be
behaviorally oriented in the rehabilitation of the hospitalized patient.
Release of patients was indeed more closely related to behavioral adjustment for the experimental-program patients than it was for the patients
of the two nonexperimental programs (see Table 4).

MARITAL STATUS. As seen in Table 4, the variable of marital
status was not found to be highly related to release. This finding is
somewhat in conflict with previous studies. Chapman et al. (1961)

found that marital status alone predicted with 62 per cent accuracy the discharge of hospitalized male patients. Patients who were never married had a much poorer chance of achieving a hospital release within nine months of their admission to the hospital.

Apparently, marital status is highly related to the premorbid adjustment level of the hospitalized patient, and for this reason the two variables are confounded. A rating of premorbid social adjustment for made admission schizophrenics was obtained by Chapman (*ibid.*) using the Elgin Prognostic Scale (Wittman, 1941). Chapman (*op. cit.*) found that not only was the Elgin scale highly related to marital status, but that both marital status and the Elgin Scale were equally predictive of release. A later study with female schizophrenic patients found similar results (Garfield and Sundland, 1966). In both studies, marital status and the Elgin Scale predicted length of hospital stay equally well.

The finding in the present study regarding the relatively low relationship between release and marital status is somewhat surprising in view of the studies cited above. Marital status was selected as an equating variable because it was anticipated that it would be highly related to outcome. One explanation may be that other studies used only admission patients, while the present study included relatively few newly admitted patients. Rather, 78 per cent of the 336 patients in the present study were hospital residents at the time the study began. Once a patient has been in the hospital for a period of time, whether or not he was once married appears to be relatively unimportant in predicting his achieving a community release.

LOBOTOMY. The history of lobotomy was not originally included as a matching variable since its relationship to release (Table 4) was not initially known. Its relationship seems partly accidental since only Group III patients had received lobotomies in any significant numbers (Table 3). Group III patients also had the lowest level of behavioral adjustment and the greatest amount of previous hospitalization, both of which are highly related to outcome. Thus, the incidence of lobotomy is probably not directly related to outcome, but appears related simply because the lobotomized patient is also likely to be poorly adjusted and chronically hospitalized.

In one study (Witton and Ellsworth, 1962) schizophrenic lobotomized patients showed significantly more confusion and paranoid ideation (MMPI Test) than a control group considered for lobotomy. Both groups had been diagnosed as schizophrenic for over 10 years, on the average. The release rate of lobotomy patients and "patients considered for but not given a lobotomy" was low and was essentially the same for both groups. For this reason, chronicity and not lobotomy is considered to be the more meaningful with respect to release outcome.

AGE. Age was not significantly related to outcome, a finding that is in keeping with other studies. Age was used as an equating variable in the present study simply because it has traditionally been reported in other studies.

THE RESULTS OF MATCHING
THE EXPERIMENTAL AND
NONEXPERIMENTAL PATIENT GROUPS

Having examined the matching variables and their relationship to outcome, one may now turn to Table 5 and our attempts to equate the experimental and nonexperimental populations on these variables. It is obvious that the three groups of Experimental and Nonexperimental Building patients were practically identical on the matching variables used in the present study. Assigning newly admitted patients to the project buildings in strict rotation did not alter the original equating of the patient populations. As seen in Table 5, there were some minor differences between the Experimental and Nonexperimental Building populations. For example, somewhat more of the Experimental Building Group III patients had had a lobotomy, had been hospitalized slightly longer, and were a little lower in behavioral adjustment at the beginning of the project. These variables were negatively related to outcome. On the other hand, slightly more of the Group III Experimental Building patients had once been married, a variable positively related to outcome. For all practical purposes the outcome probability, as related to these matching variables, is essentially the same for the experimental and nonexperimental patients.

As mentioned earlier, the purpose of equating the groups of Experimental and Nonexperimental Building patients was to insure that differences in outcome between the programs would reflect differences in treatment effectiveness. If the patient groups had not been equated, one would expect differences in outcome to the extent that those variables related to outcome were uncontrolled. The results, to be reported in the next chapter, are clearly not a function of any differences in the background or initial adjustment characteristics of the patients exposed to the experimental and nonexperimental programs.

Table 5 - Similarity of Schizophrenic Patient Groups with Respect to Chronicity, Behavioral Adjustment, Marital Status, Lobotomy and Age

		Group I Patients	Group II Patients	Group III Patients
Chronicity (Amount Hospitalized during last 5 years)	Experimental Building Patients	7.6 months*	45.7 months*	12.2 years*
	Nonexperimental Building Patients	8.9 months*	44.8 months*	11.7 years*
Behavioral Adjustment (MACC Scale raw score)	Experimental Building Patients	65.32	62.84	56.47
	Nonexperimental Building Patients	65.54	62.92	58.04
Marital Status (once married)	Experimental Building Patients	40%	19%	17%
	Nonexperimental Building Patients	41%	25%	11%
Lobotomy	Experimental Building Patients	0%	6%	40%
	Nonexperimental Building Patients	1%	8%	27%
Age	Experimental Building Patients	36.8 years	37.8 years	44.8 years
	Nonexperimental Building Patients	36.2 years	39.9 years	44.3 years

* Total amount of hospitalization is reported for Group III patients, while the amount of hospitalization during the immediately preceding five years is reported for the Group I and Group II patients.

SUMMARY

As pointed out in this chapter, several aspects of the aide role were modified, and this general role change is regarded as the experimental variable. In addition to the already reported increase in the aide-patient interaction level, the aides' level of participation in, and satisfaction with, team meetings was found to increase significantly in the experimental program. It was also suggested that the patients' perception of the aide's status increased, although this was not measured.

No single criterion, by itself, is adequate to measure the impact of the aide role change on patient rehabilitation. Several possible methods for judging program effectiveness are discussed, including both in-hospital and community measures. It was also pointed out that the differential impact of the experimental programs should be examined as it affected a wide range of chronic and acute, young and old, well-adjusted and poorly-adjusted patients. Patient groups in the experimental and nonexperimental programs were matched on several variables related to treatment outcome. Three groups of schizophrenic patients emerged, each of which differed with respect to the probability of achieving a release; the acute or Group I patients, the semi-chronic or Group II patients, and the chronic or Group III patients. These groups differed not only on the probability of achieving a release, but also on amount of previous hospitalization, behavioral adjustment, marital status, age, and incidence of lobotomy. The first two of these variables were found to be most highly predictive of a significant release.

The impact of the experimental and nonexperimental programs on each group of patients will be presented in the next two chapters. Since each of the three patient groups in the experimental and nonexperimental programs were carefully matched on those variables related to significant release, differences in treatment outcome between the programs can be attributed only to their differential effectiveness.

7

Results of In-Hospital Measures of Treatment Effectiveness

The treatment results of the experimental and nonexperimental programs will be discussed separately for each group of schizophrenic patients. Group I (acute group) represents those schizophrenic patients with the least amount of hospitalization (zero to two years out of the preceding five years); Group II (semi-chronic), those with between two and five years hospitalization during the preceding five years; and Group III (chronic) those who have been continuously hospitalized during the preceding five years. Not only do these groups differ on such characteristics as behavioral adjustment, marital status, and age, but they also differ with respect to treatment outcome. For example, of all Group III patients in the experimental and nonexperimental program, the typical or median patient never reached the community during the 915 project days. The median or typical Group I patient, however, reached the community within 96 days of entering the project.

This chapter will first report the treatment results of such "in-hospital" criteria as behavioral adjustment change, proportions of patients reaching the community, and length of hospital stay during the project. These data should be regarded as "soft data" in comparison with the community follow-up data. In other words, the in-hospital data are those that are subject to "control" by the hospital staff (i.e., motivation of the staff to release patients early, bias in the behavioral ratings, and the like). Although the possibility of rarter bias exists, the behavioral adjustment improvement for patients in the experimental program does coincide with the previously described clinical evolution of the program itself. As explained in Chapter 5, the increased adjustment level of experimental ward patients led to the development of a second open ward, a decrease in the failure rate of patients transferred from the closed to the open ward, an increase of earned privileges on the remaining closed ward, and finally, the ability of the open-ward patients to handle increasingly complex activity assignments. From these program changes

110

alone, it seems obvious that the patient groups did improve from a clinical standpoint. The behavioral adjustment score changes of the experimental-program patients, then, reflect this improvement. The possibility still exists, however, that the behavioral ratings reflected both program change and rater bias. It is because of this, that the behavioral rating data should be regarded as "soft data."

With regard to staff motivation of the Experimental and Nonexperimental Units, there clearly were changes during the project period. The professional staff of these units were in competition with each other. The staff of one Nonexperimental Unit voiced this competitive feeling. The physician said, for example, "We are out to beat your (Experimental Unit) results," and did in fact succeed in significantly improving his units' release rates. Schizophrenic admissions had a 70 per cent chance of achieving a release within the first year after their admission for the period 1955–58. Within one year after this project started (1959–60), the release rate increased for both the Experimental and Nonexperimental Units, with 84 per cent of these patients achieving a release within the first year of admission (see Ellsworth and Stokes, 1963).

The release rates for the chronically hospitalized schizophrenic reflected, even more clearly, changes in overall operations of the hospital during these two periods. Patients hospitalized continuously in the pre-study period (1955–58) had a 5 per cent chance of achieving a hospital release within the 30-month period. As will be seen later in this chapter, the chronically hospitalized patient, during the period of this study, had a 25 per cent chance of achieving a release from the Nonexperimental units, and a 59 per cent chance on the Experimental Unit.

Thus, the changes in hospital release rates were affected, at least in part, by the stimulus of competition between the units. Were the differential release rates between units also a reflection of a greater motivation to discharge in the experimental unit staff? Two facts suggest that this was not the case. First, the chief of psychiatric service, who took part in the discharge planning of each patient and who gave the final approval for all proposed releases, served as a kind of control on discharge criterion. Second, the experimental program, while releasing significantly more Group II and Group III patients than the nonexperimental program, did not have a greater return rate. When differences in return rate occurred they were somewhat higher for the Nonexperimental Units. These release-rate differences between the Experimental and Nonexperimental Units, then, do not appear to be a function of the motivation of the Experimental Unit staff to release patients before the patients were ready.

At the time the research program started, the hospital adopted the unit system of operation in which more of the decision-making responsibility was given to the unit teams. There is no doubt that had a centralized decision-making operation continued, it would have seriously restricted the flow of patients into and out of the hospital. The increase of discharge rates for all groups of patients in the hospital as a whole was undoubtedly a function of both the adoption of the unit system of operation, and the feeling of competition stimulated by the research program itself. Declassification or mixing of poorly-adjusted and well-adjusted patients, however, did little to improve the overall level of behavioral adjustment of the long-term patients in the nonexperimental programs (see next section). Thus, the introduction of the unclassified-unit system in the two Nonexperimental Units resulted in an increase in efficiency with regard to the admission and discharge of patients, but had no measurable effect on the behavioral adjustment of the chronically hospitalized patient groups in these unclassified units. The research unit, whose three wards were classified on the basis of behavioral adjustment, was successful in increasing the behavioral adjustment level of its chronically hospitalized patients.

BEHAVIORAL ADJUSTMENT CHANGES

Noted in Chapter 6, behavioral adjustment changes were recorded throughout the study, using the MACC Behavioral Adjustment rating scale (Ellsworth, 1962). This scale was designed to be completed by any observer of the patient's behavior who demonstrates acceptable reliability. In the present study, the evening-shift aides were trained in the use of the scale. Upon completion of rater-reliability studies, those aides who demonstrated the greatest stability of scores on two successive ratings of a group of 10 to 15 patients became the permanent raters for the project. All raters chosen remained on the same shift and building throughout the evaluation period. The evening-shift aides were chosen primarily because: 1) they were not directly involved in the treatment program of the Experimental and Nonexperimental Buildings as were the day-shift aides, and were therefore more likely to be objective in their ratings; 2) they were able to evaluate the residual effects of the program by observing only those behaviors that carried over to the evening period; and 3) they were in a position to observe the behavior of all patients for at least four to six hours each day. The use of behavioral adjustment changes represents an "in-hospital" measure of program effectiveness.

In presenting the behavioral adjustment changes for each group of patients in the experimental and nonexperimental programs, certain problems arise. Although most patients entered the project on March 1, 1959 (i.e., the 262 resident patients), 74 additional Group I and Group II patients entered the project between March 1, 1959 and March 1, 1960 upon their admission to the hospital. In presenting the initial behavioral adjustment scores for each cohort of Group I, Group II, and Group III experimental and nonexperimental patients, then, a behavioral adjustment rating was obtained for each patient as he entered the project. For most patients, this initial rating was obtained on March 1, 1959. For those who entered the hospital after that date, a behavioral adjustment rating was obtained at the time of their admission to the hospital.

The average behavioral adjustment score changes are presented for each cohort of patients as a function of time in the project. For example, how were a cohort of experimental patients rated, on admission, two months later, four months later, six months later, and so on, as compared with a similar cohort of nonexperimental patients? The problem here was that all patients in each cohort did not remain in the hospital to be rated at these times. Some Group I patients, for example, left the hospital within one month of their admission to the project. It was decided that if a patient left the hospital prior to the next scheduled rating period, an *exit rating* would be obtained for him, a rating which described his behavioral adjustment at the time of his release from the hospital. If a patient returned to the hospital, his rating was resumed at regularly scheduled intervals.

Another problem was how to reflect the behavioral adjustment scores of patients who were no longer in the hospital. For those patients who left the hospital, it was decided to use their exit rating as the best estimate of their current adjustment level, and to discontinue entirely the ratings for each cohort once approximately half of them had left the hospital. To have used the scores of only those who remained in the hospital would have disregarded the behavioral changes of patients who had improved and had left the hospital as a result of the programs. On the other hand, to have continued to report the behavioral adjustment changes for each cohort beyond the time when less than half of the patients in that cohort were being currently rated would have made it unlikely that the average behavioral adjustment scores for that cohort would have reflected much change. Even if those few patients who remained in the hospital had changed a great deal, the average change for the entire cohort would have been small.

BEHAVIORAL ADJUSTMENT CHANGES OF GROUP I PATIENTS. The Group I patient cohort was rated at the time of admission to the project and every two months thereafter. As presented in Table 3, 60 per cent of Group I patients entered the project after March 1, 1959. As they were admitted to the hospital, as already noted, they were assigned to one of the three buildings in strict rotation. By four months after admission to the project, more than half of this Group I cohort had left the hospital. It was decided, therefore, to report only two ratings for Group I patients, the admission rating and the release or four-month rating. In looking back, it is recognized that it would have been better to rate each Group I patient every month. This would have permitted a better estimate of the rapidity of behavioral change for this group of patients.

Table 6 shows that the rotation-assignment procedure resulted in highly similar Group I experimental and nonexperimental patients from the standpoint of behavioral adjustment. The average admission behavioral adjustment score of the experimental Group I patients was 65.32 (± 12.86), while the average of the nonexperimental group was 65.54 (± 11.25).

By the time of the second rating, both the experimental and nonexperimental Group I patients had shown a significant gain in their MACC ratings. The experimental Group I patients, however, showed a greater gain in their adjustment scores than the patients in the nonexperimental programs (t 2.61, significant beyond the .01 level).

From the data presented in Table 6, it would appear that the Group I patient was able to modify his behavioral adjustment to a greater extent in the experimental program than in the nonexperimental programs. As explained earlier, the experimental program was actually designed to approach the patient in terms of his level of behavioral adjustment. This not only allowed the psychiatric aide to work with the patient in terms of helping him modify his daily behavior, but it also permitted the patient to move from the closed to the open and discharge ward as his behavioral adjustment improved.

In contrast, the typical patient on the nonexperimental wards lived in the same large ward throughout his hospital stay. Unlike the experimental program patient, he did not move through different wards where a progressively higher level of behavioral adjustment was expected and reinforced. The patient in the Nonexperimental Units was allowed to remain on the open wards as long as he did not create a disturbance, and was transferred to a locked security ward only if he could not handle himself. The experimental patient, however, had to earn, through his im-

Table 6 - Average Behavioral Adjustment Scores of Experimental and Non-
     experimental Group I Patients at Time of Admission and Again at
                    Discharge or Four Months

	Admission Ratings	Discharge or Four-Month Rating	Average Increase	t Value
MACC Score, Experimental Group I Patients (N = 38)	65.32 (60 per- centile)	73.10 (86 per- centile)	7.78	4.76**
MACC Score, Nonexperimental Group I Patients (N = 66)	65.54 (60 per- centile)	68.27 (71 per- centile)	2.73	2.99*
Difference Between Experimental and Nonexperimental Patients	.22	4.83		
t Value	.12	2.61⁴		

* Significant beyond the .01 level of confidence.

** Significant beyond the .001 level of confidence,

proved behavior, the increased freedom and privileges of the open and discharge ward. He was not permitted to remain on the open ward, let alone the discharge ward, simply by staying out of trouble. Rather, his status on each ward was determined by his ability to meet the expectations for that ward regarding activity assignments, socialization, and self-care. In the writer's opinion, this expectation for progressively improved behavior, built into both the philosophy and structure of the experimental program, would best explain the higher level of behavioral adjustment attained by the experimental Group I patients in contrast to those on the Nonexperimental Units.

BEHAVIORAL ADJUSTMENT CHANGES OF GROUP II AND GROUP III PATIENTS. The Group II and Group III cohorts were rated at the time they entered the project, and every four months thereafter. Previous experience (see Ellsworth *et al.*, 1958) had indicated that the more chronically hospitalized patient changes rather slowly in his behavioral adjustment level, and that the rate of behavioral change can be documented by having him rated every four months. After 24 months, the ratings of Group II and Group III patients was discontinued. By this time, approximately 40 to 50 per cent of the experimental Group II and Group III patients had left the hospital. This meant that by the end of the 24-month period, a good proportion of the behavioral rating scores represented a continuation of the last rating before release. If a significant change in program effectiveness had occurred, the behavioral adjustment averages for the total group would hardly have reflected this change since many scores, obtained at the time of the patient's exit from the hospital, were carried over as the best estimate of the patient's current adjustment level.

As seen in Figures 2 and 3, the experimental program chronic and semi-chronic patients showed a steady and significant progression in their behavioral adjustment levels. This was not true of similar patients in the Nonexperimental Units. One of the most interesting features of the data presented in Figure 3 is the length of time it took for the Group III experimental patients to become better adjusted than their nonexperimental counterparts. As mentioned earlier, one cannot expect marked behavioral improvement in regressed, chronically hospitalized patients unless one works with them for at least a year in an effective and well-structured program. As seen later, significantly more of the experimental than nonexperimental Group III patients were able to leave the hospital after only some 18 months of participation in the program.

The lack of behavioral improvement of the nonexperimental Group II and Group III patients is rather puzzling, especially since their Group I patients did show significant behavioral improvement. One likely explanation, based on our observations of the acute and chronic patient, was that the acute patient was better able to seek out and relate to people in this environment. The chronically hospitalized patient, on the other hand, was generally withdrawn to the point where he did not assume the initiative for establishing these relationships. Indeed, he tended to remain uninvolved even when an attempt was made to initiate contact with him. What seemed to be necessary in order for the more chronic patient to show a significant behavioral improvement was a constant, repetitive, ongoing intrusion into his world. It was our observation that this intrusion, if it is to be effective, must occur regularly and consistently. In the experimental program, through interaction with the aide, demands were made on the chronic patient that he participate with the aide or other patients in activities. Also, the staff's perception

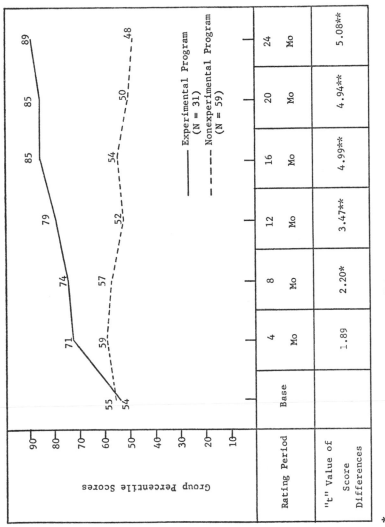

Rating Period	Base	4 Mo	8 Mo	12 Mo	16 Mo	20 Mo	24 Mo
"t" Value of Score Differences		1.89	2.20*	3.47**	4.99**	4.94**	5.08**

*Significant beyond the .05 level of confidence.
**Significant beyond the .01 level of confidence.

Fig. 2. MACC behavioral adjustment changes of experimental and nonexperimental Group II semi-chronic schizophrenics.

117

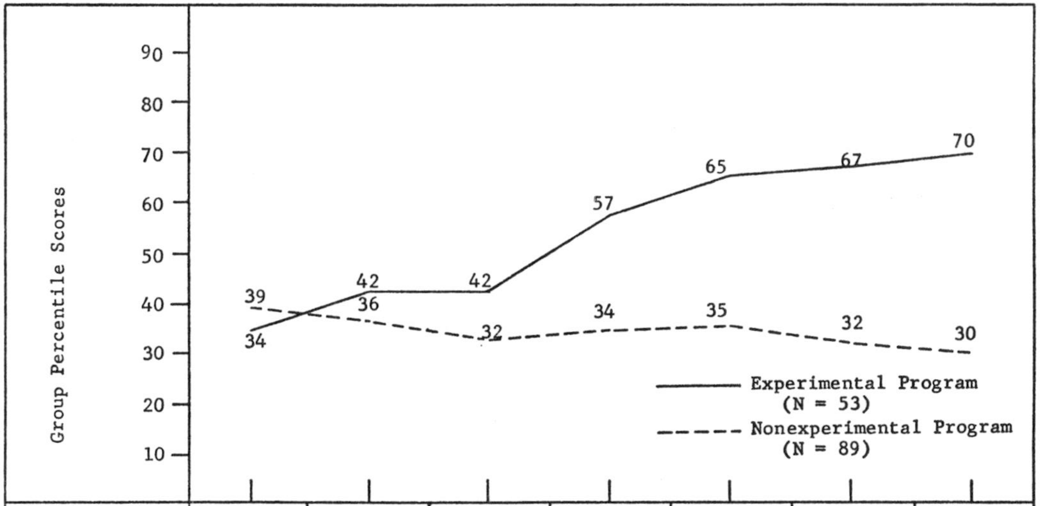

*Significant beyond .001 level of confidence.

Fig. 3. MACC behavioral adjustment changes of experimental and nonexperimental Group III chronic schizophrenics.

and expectations of the chronic patient were reviewed with him in the weekly ward team meetings. Without this constant intrusion and feed-back, the gains made by the chronically hospitalized groups would prob-ably not have occurred.

DISCHARGE RATE OF EXPERIMENTAL AND NONEXPERIMENTAL PATIENTS

The release-rate data are reported here primarily because they con-stitute a traditional criterion of treatment outcome. At a time when psychiatric hospitals were custodially centered, the release of a patient was an important event. More recently, the vast majority of patients admitted to mental hospitals can expect to be released. This criterion, while an important indication of treatment efficiency, is no longer an adequate measure of hospital program effectiveness, especially for re-cently admitted patients. Rather, in evaluating psychiatric programs, the adequacy of community adjustment following hospitalization constitutes a much better measure of treatment effectiveness for such patients. The release of a long term chronically hospitalized patient, however, is still regarded by many hospital personnel as an important indication of pro-gram effectiveness.

The release rates reported here occurred under the stabilizing in-fluence of the chief of psychiatric service, who, as already indicated, ap-proved the release of all hospitalized patients. His consistent influence on all units regarding readiness for release lends some meaning to these data. Noted earlier, the release rates of schizophrenic patients for the entire hospital rose significantly during the study period. The probabil-ity of release over a 30-month period was 72 per cent for Group I, 31 per cent for Group II, and 5 per cent for Group III, for the three years prior to this research. During the 30 months of the project, the release rates for experimental and nonexperimental patients were 91 per cent of all Group I, 69 per cent of Group II, and 38 per cent of all Group III patients. There can be no doubt that the impact of the study on the operational efficiency of the hospital was a highly significant one.

The rates of release are presented in Figures 4, 5, and 6 as a func-tion of time. Release-rate differences between experimental and non-experimental programs are tested for statistical significance later in this chapter. From Figure 4 it is apparent that the Group I patient obtained his release from the experimental program somewhat more quickly than did the patient in the nonexperimental program. By the end of the 22 months, however, just as many nonexperimental Group I patients had obtained their first release from the hospital as had the experimental Group I patients. Perhaps the most significant finding suggested in Figure 4 is that the experimental program released its Group I patients within a shorter period of time than did the nonexperimental program. The beds of the Experimental Unit were made available more quickly for occupancy by new patients. In fact, some 14 beds were taken from the Experimental Unit during the project because they were not being used, and were redistributed on the Nonexperimental Units.

Figure 5 shows that the experimental program released its Group II patients earlier and in greater numbers throughout the project period. At the 14th month, 62 per cent of the experimental and 41 per cent of the nonexperimental Group II cohort had reached the community, a difference of 21 per cent. Continuing to lose ground by the 24th month, the nonexperimental program had released 59 per cent of its patient cohort, compared with 86 per cent for the experimental program, a difference of 27 per cent.

Figure 6 presents the release-rate data for the experimental and nonexperimental Group III patients. It was not until the 16th month that more of the experimental chronic patient cohort began to achieve release than their nonexperimental counterparts. By the 26th month, 57 per cent of the experimental and 21 per cent of the nonexperimental cohort had been released, a difference of 36 per cent. With chronically hospitalized patients the differential effects of the experimental program were not reflected by release until after they had achieved and maintained a significantly higher level of behavioral adjustment than their nonexperimental counterparts. It is to be recalled from Figure 3 that the experimental cohort achieved a significantly better adjustment than the nonexperimental Group III patient by the 12th month. Obviously, the chronically hospitalized patient's release from the hospital requires a good deal of additional planning after his reaching a higher level of behavioral functioning. This is less true of the acute patient who usually leaves the hospital shortly after his level of functioning has improved.

From the data presented in Figures 4, 5, and 6, it would appear that the experimental program not only released more patients than the Nonexperimental programs, but that the experimental patient spent less time in the hospital prior to release as compared with his nonexperimental counterpart. These data, however, must be tested for statistical significance in order to examine the possibility that these differences could have arisen by chance. The data in Table 7 present the number of days of hospital-treatment time for each of the groups during the 30-month

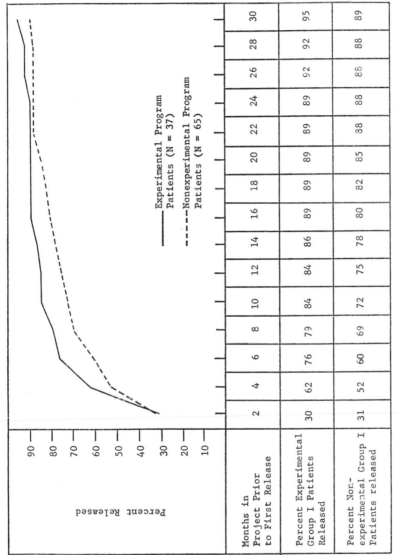

Months in Project Prior to First Release	2	4	6	8	10	12	14	16	18	20	22	24	26	28	30
Percent Experimental Group I Patients Released	30	62	76	79	84	84	86	89	89	89	89	89	92	92	95
Percent Non-experimental Group I Patients released	31	52	60	69	72	75	78	80	82	85	88	88	88	88	89

——— Experimental Program Patients (N = 37)

-----Nonexperimental Program Patients (N = 65)

Percent Released

Fig. 4. Months Group I patients spent in the project prior to a first release (excluding two patients who died).

121

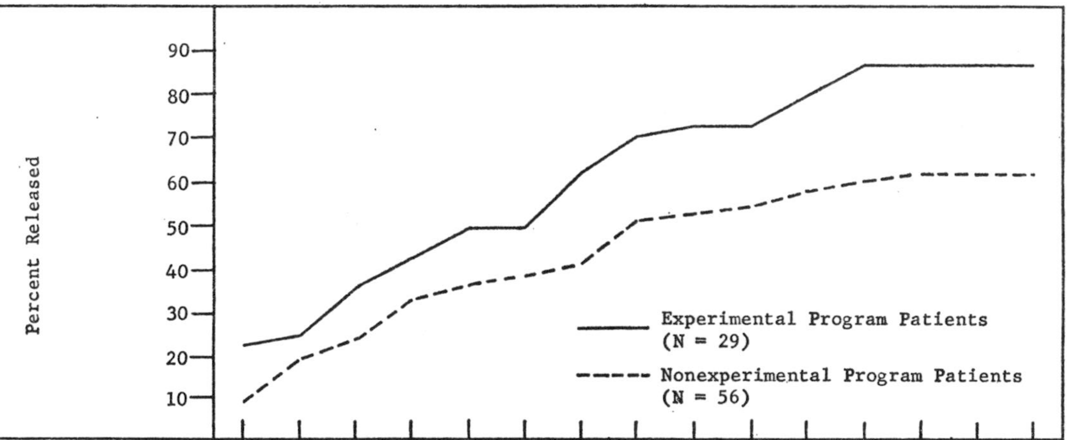

Months in Project to First Release	2	4	6	8	10	12	14	16	18	20	22	24	26	28	30
Percent Experimental Group II Patients Released	21	24	35	41	48	48	62	69	72	72	79	86	86	86	86
Percent Non-experimental Group II Patients Released	7	18	23	32	36	38	41	50	52	54	57	59	61	61	61

Experimental Program Patients (N = 29)

Nonexperimental Program Patients (N = 56)

Fig. 5. Months Group II patients spent in the project prior to a first release (excluding five patients who died).

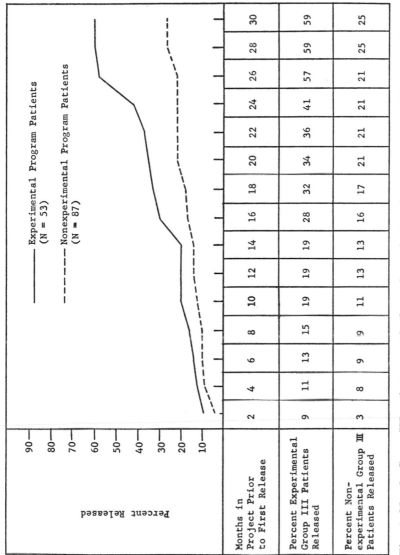

Months in Project Prior to First Release	2	4	6	8	10	12	14	16	18	20	22	24	26	28	30
Percent Experimental Group III Patients Released	9	11	13	15	19	19	19	28	32	34	36	41	57	59	59
Percent Non-experimental Group III Patients Released	3	8	9	9	11	13	13	16	17	21	21	21	21	25	25

——— Experimental Program Patients (N = 53)

- - - - Nonexperimental Program Patients (N = 87)

Percent Released

Fig. 6. Months Group III patients spent in the project prior to a first release (excluding two patients who died).

123

Table 7 - Number of Days Patients Received Hospital Treatment During 30-Month Period
(Excluding 9 patients who died)

		Group I		Group II		Group III		Totals
Mean Days Hospitalized	Experimental	297.0		576.2		697.7		
	Nonexperimental	359.7		674.7		833.5		
Median Days Hospitalized	Experimental	238		609		789		
	Nonexperimental	285		836		915		
Statistical Test of Differences		Shorter than Combined Median	Longer than Combined Median	Shorter than Combined Median	Longer than Combined Median	Shorter than Combined Median	Longer than Combined Median	
Percent of Group	Experimental	54%	46%	66%	34%	58%	42%	
	Nonexperimental	48%	52%	41%	59%	25%	75%	
Number of Group	Experimental	20	17	19	10	31	22	119
	Nonexperimental	31	34	23	33	22	65	208
Cell Square Contingency		.19		1.40		11.15		20.75
				3.15		4.67		
Level of Significance		N.S.		N.S.		.001		.001
						.05		

124

or 915-day project period. If the patient left the hospital and returned within the 915-day period, the additional number of rehospitalization days was recorded.

In the experimental program, the Group I, II and III patients required, on the average, 63, 99, and 136 fewer days of hospitalization, respectively, than did their counterparts in the Nonexperimental Units. Statistical tests of the median differences were computed because of the skewness of the distribution. The combined chi square of 20.75 indicates that these hospital-treatment-time differences between the experimental and nonexperimental programs could have arisen by chance less than one in 1,000 times ($<.001$ for five degrees of freedom). An examination of the contingency values for each group of patients, however, reveals that the main effect of the experimental program occurred with the Group II and Group III patients. Significantly more of the experimental Group III patients were released from the hospital early, while significantly more of the nonexperimental patients remained beyond 915 days. More of the nonexperimental Group II patients also stayed beyond the median length of stay, but this just missed significance at the .05 level. As judged by the criterion of total treatment days, the experimental program appears to have had a greater impact on the more chronically hospitalized patients.

In an experiment as large and comprehensive as this, multiple tests of significance cannot be avoided. It is desirable, however, to perform one test of significance for each set of outcome data by combining all patient groups. The Cell Square Contingency method (Guilford, 1956, pp. 337–340) allows one to test a set of data for overall significance. If a significant overall treatment effect is found, then one is able to examine the significance of each group's contribution toward the total chi square value.

The use of the Cell Square Contingency method in this study, however, would not be appropriate if the three groups of patients were disproportionately represented in the experimental and nonexperimental programs. If, for example, 50 per cent of the Experimental and 20 per cent of the Nonexperimental Units' patients were Group III patients, a test of the release-outcome data for all groups combined would be difficult to interpret. Since the chronic group have the lowest release expectancy, a similar overall release rate between programs would actually mean that the experimental program was more effective than the nonexperimental in releasing patients. Fortunately, however, the proportion of Group I, II, and III patients in each program is almost identical (see Table 1, page 100). The Cell Square Contingency method, then, represents an appropriate statistical technique for testing the significance of treatment outcome differences between experimental and nonexperimental programs.

Table 8 - Number of Experimental and Nonexperimental Schizophrenic Patients Reaching the Community During the 30-Month Project (Excluding 9 patients who died)

		Group I		Group II		Group III		Total
		Not Released	Released	Not Released	Released	Not Released	Released	
Percent of Group	Experimental	5%	95%	14%	86%	41%	59%	
	Nonexperimental	11%	89%	39%	61%	75%	25%	
Number of Group	Experimental	2	35	4	25	22	31	119
	Nonexperimental	7	58	22	34	65	22	208
Cell Square	Experimental	.51	.04	3.18	.57	2.97	7.09	14.36
	Nonexperimental	.30	.02	1.83	.33	1.70	4.06	8.24
Contingency	Sum	.81	.06	5.01	.90	4.67	11.15	22.60
Level of Significance		N.S.	N.S.	$<.05$	N.S.	$<.05$	$<.001$	$<.001$

Table 8 presents the release-rate data for each group of patients in the experimental and nonexperimental programs. As seen here, the overall release rate of the experimental program is significantly higher than that of the nonexperimental program (chi square = 22.60, p. < .001 for 5 degrees of freedom). The primary contributions to this significant chi square come from the higher release rate of Group III experimental program patients, and the higher "not released" rate of Group II and Group III patients from the Nonexperimental programs. As a matter of fact, as many of the Group III experimental patient cohort (59 per cent) were released from the experimental program as were the nonexperimental patients in the Group II cohort (61 per cent). In light of the poorer prognosis for release of the Group III patient as compared with the Group II patient, this finding again suggests that the experimental program was highly effective with its chronically hospitalized group of patients.

SUMMARY

During the 30 months of the project, the release rates of all groups of schizophrenic patients rose significantly as compared with the release rates which had been characteristic for the hospital before the study started. Thus the impact of the study itself was hospital-wide. With regard to such in-hospital measures of treatment effectiveness as behavioral-adjustment changes, differences favored the experimental program. Although the behavioral adjustment level of all Group I acute schizophrenics improved, the experimental Group I patients' adjustment level increased more than their counterparts in the nonexperimental program. The level of behavioral adjustment for the Group II and Group III patients improved significantly for the experimental patients only after several months of program operation, but did not increase for the nonexperimental Group II and Group III patients. Thus, the more chronically hospitalized patient not only improves slowly, but improves only in that program designed to affect his behavioral adjustment.

With regard to differences in length of stay and release rates for the experimental and nonexperimental patients, it was found that more of the experimental Group II and Group III patients left the hospital, and in a shorter period of time, than did their counterparts in the nonexperimental buildings. No significant differences in release rate or time-in-hospital (including rehospitalization time) was found for the Group I patients in the experimental and nonexperimental programs. In this respect the experimental program appears to have a differential effect on the more chronically hospitalized groups of patients.

The data presented in this chapter are subject, in part, to staff bias (i.e., staff influence upon behavioral adjustment ratings and discharge rates). Although certain procedures were used to control for these influences, they must, nevertheless, be regarded as "soft" data. Such data as return rates and post-hospital adjustment, however, are not subject to these influences. These data are presented in the next chapter.

8

Community Measures of Treatment
Effectiveness of Released Patients

Originally, a total of 336 patients entered the project. During the 30-month project period, nine of these died, leaving a total of 327 patients on whom outcome data were collected. The data in the previous chapter reported such "in-hospital" measures of treatment effectiveness as behavioral adjustment changes, release rates, and days of hospitalization for each group. This chapter examines the treatment outcome for these 327 experimental and nonexperimental patients from the standpoint of their success or failure in adjusting to the community.

Referring back to Table 8, p. 126, the number of patients released from the experimental program was significantly greater than that released from the nonexperimental units, especially for the Group II and Group III patients. It has been found, however, that a program which does nothing more than simply release a greater number of its patients within a given period of time will have a proportionately higher return rate (see Zolik and Lantz, 1965). A program that releases more patients than would normally be expected could achieve this result by discharging a larger share of poor risks who were not ready to return to the community. If a hospital program has not had a real impact on modifying the behavior of the more poorly adjusted patient, but has simply released him unimproved into the community, one would expect that the return rate would be higher for that hospital.

The ability of professional staff to predict with complete success the poor risks from the good risks is questionable (Lasky et al., 1959). As will be seen later in this chapter, few, if any, investigators have been able to predict which patients will return, although one can often predict community adjustment at the time of discharge. The patient, however, who has remained hospitalized for a prolonged period of time is often presumed to be a poor risk even if he has demonstrated a high level of behavioral adjustment and an ability to care for himself. During

129

the project, both the Experimental and Nonexperimental Unit staffs had a great deal of difficulty in convincing the chief of psychiatric service that a chronically hospitalized but behaviorally well-adjusted Group III patient should be released. However, the return rate of this chronically hospitalized group was no higher than that of the acute Group I (or presumably good-risk) patient.

The Group III patient who had shown a great deal of *recent* behavioral and symptomatic improvement as a result of the experimental program represented an even larger problem in that it was especially difficult to obtain permission for his release. The chief of psychiatric service, who had known these patients for years, knew them as unchanging and poorly adjusted. He assumed that the patient he had known in 1958 was essentially the same patient in 1960. Since he had not observed the day-to-day changes occurring in many of these patients, he would react to the proposed release of a previously poorly adjusted chronic patient by saying, "You can't be serious, that man is crazy." The ward staff, who felt that these patients had changed and were ready for release, became very frustrated in trying to deal with his objections. Often the chief of service and the ward staff were talking about two different people; Patient X as he was in 1958, and Patient X as he was in 1960.

If a program is operating effectively, a large number of chronically hospitalized patients should be released as a function of their improvement. Under such circumstances, the return rate should be no greater than would be typical of an ineffective program that released only its best patients. A program, however, which is both ineffective *and* which discharges a high proportion of its population, will probably experience an upswing in its return rate, as suggested by Zolik and Lantz (1965).

In contrast to the data presented in Chapter 7, the data presented in this chapter are to be regarded as "hard data," i.e., data that cannot be influenced by such factors as staff bias. The return rates and level of community adjustment, for example, are determined not by the hospital staff, but by the patient and his community.

AMOUNT OF HOSPITALIZATION PRIOR TO A FIRST SIGNIFICANT RELEASE

Achieving a hospital release is a function of several factors, including staff motivation to discharge. A release *followed* by a prolonged community stay, however, is a much better reflection of treatment program effectiveness than release alone. Gurel (1966) has found that the amount of time a patient spent in the hospital, prior to a release followed by 90 consecutive days in the community, is highly related to a wide variety of treatment-outcome criteria. His statistic FSR-90 defines as the first significant release (SR) one that is followed by 90 consecutive days in the community.

In the present study, a significant release is defined as a release followed by 12 consecutive months in the community (SR-1 year). The amount of hospitalization during the project, required to reach an SR-1 year, is recorded for each patient. If a patient left the hospital after 60 days of project hospitalization and returned again in four months, he had not achieved an SR-1 year. Upon return, he might require an additional 60 days of project hospitalization before being again released. If this second release is followed by 365 days in the community, then he is recorded as achieving an SR-1 year. For this patient, then, 120 days of project hospitalization were required before an SR-1 year was achieved. Since an SR includes the return and amount of rehospitalization following a community failure, it is presented as hard data. The staff may discharge a patient, but unless he is ready for discharge he will not ordinarily achieve an SR-1 year.

In presenting these data on SR-1 year, if the patient returned to any hospital, this stay is also recorded. Through contact with friends, relatives, VA contact officers, and VA regional offices, we were able to learn the whereabouts of all experimental and nonexperimental patients leaving the Fort Meade Hospital.

Figure 7 presents as a function of hospital treatment time, the proportion of Group I patients who achieved an SR-1 year. Within four months of project hospital treatment, approximately 50 per cent of the experimental Group I patients had achieved release followed by at least 12 consecutive months in the community. The typical or median nonexperimental patient, however, did not obtain his SR-1 year until after eight months of hospital-treatment time. The median Group II experimental patient (Figure 8) obtained a release, followed by one year in the community, within 23 months of hospital-treatment time after entering the project. The typical or median nonexperimental Group II patient never achieved an SR-1 year during the entire project. Rather, only about one third of these nonexperimental patients achieved a 12-month release. This difference between programs was also found with the Group III patients (Figure 9). The median Group III patient in the experimental program achieved a release followed by 12 months in the community within 28 months of project hospitalization. Only 16 per cent of the nonexperimental Group III patients achieved an SR-1 year during the 30-month project.

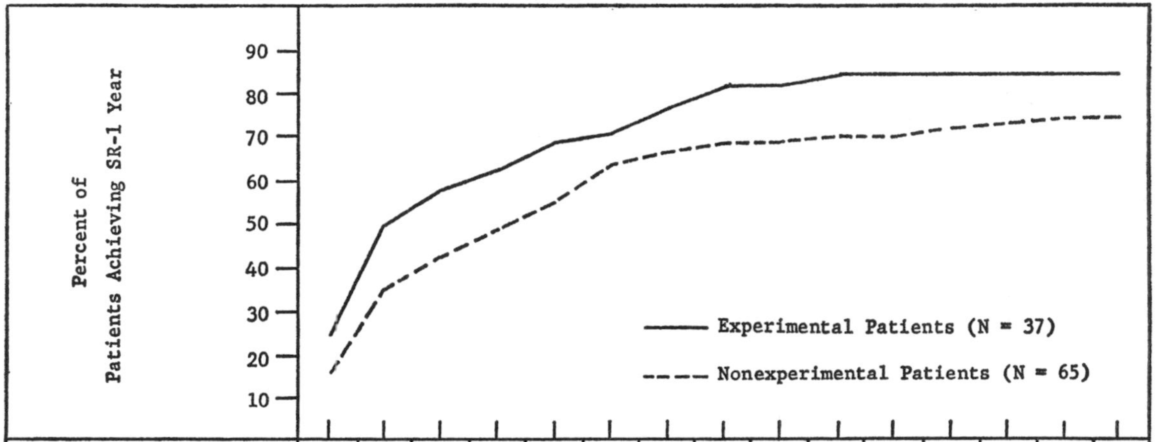

Percent of
Patients Achieving SR-1 Year

— Experimental Patients (N = 37)

- - - - Nonexperimental Patients (N = 65)

Months in Project Hospitalization Prior to SR-1 Year	2	4	6	8	10	12	14	16	18	20	22	24	26	28	30
Percent Experimental Patients Achieving SR-1 Year	24	49	57	62	68	70	76	81	81	84	84	84	84	84	84
Percent Nonexperimental Patients Achieving SR-1 Year	15	34	42	48	54	63	66	68	68	69	69	71	72	74	74
Differences in Percentages	9	15	15	14	14	7	10	13	13	15	15	13	12	10	10

Fig. 7. The amount of hospitalization for Group I patients prior to a significant release (SR-1 year).

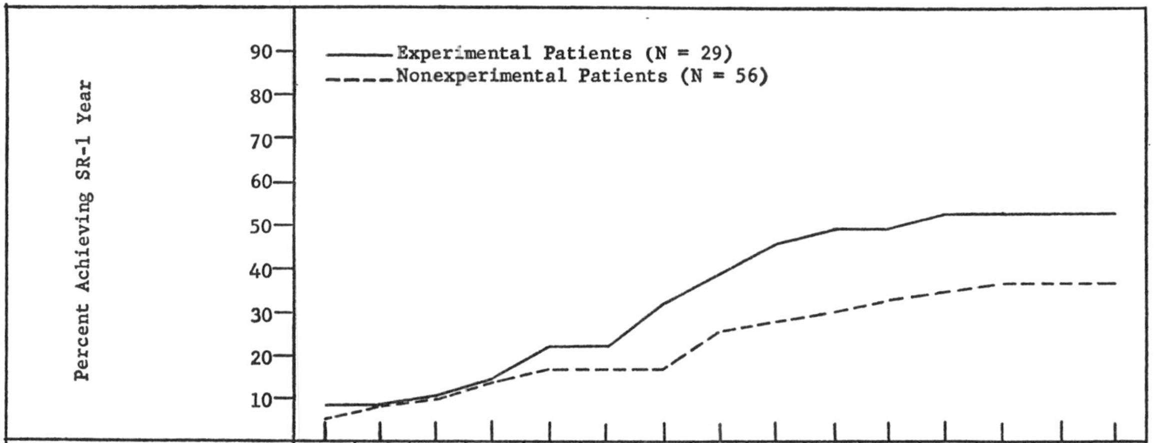

Months of Project Hospitalization Prior to SR-1 Year	2	4	6	8	10	12	14	16	18	20	22	24	26	28	30
Percent Experimental Patients Achieving SR-1 Year	7	7	10	14	21	21	31	38	45	48	48	52	52	52	52
Percent Nonexperimental Patients Achieving SR-1 Year	4	7	9	13	16	16	16	25	27	29	32	34	36	36	36
Differences in Percentages	3	0	1	1	5	5	15	13	18	19	16	18	16	16	16

Fig. 8. The amount of hospitalization for Group II patients prior to a significant release (SR-1 year).

133

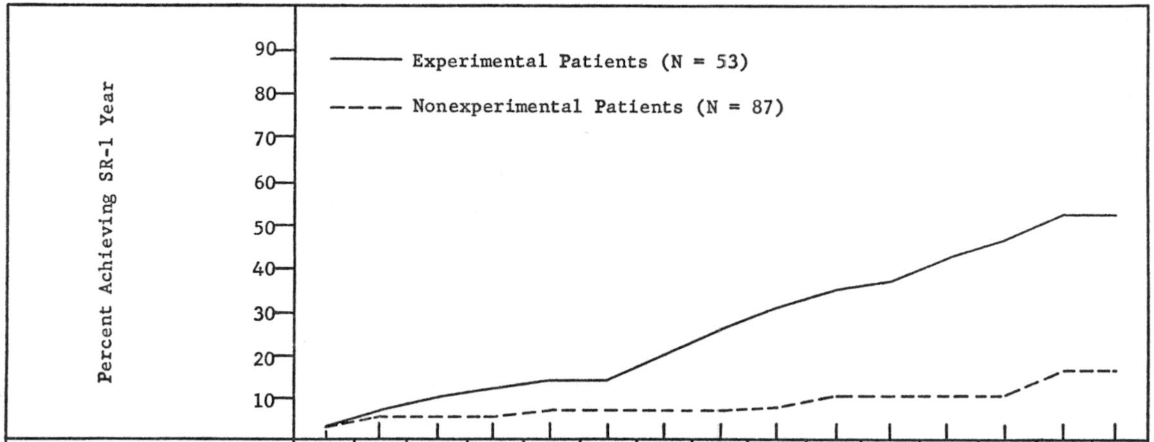

Months of Project Hospitalization Prior to SR-1 Year	2	4	6	8	10	12	14	16	18	20	22	24	26	28	30
Percent Experimental Patients Achieving SR-1 Year	2	6	8	11	13	13	19	25	30	34	36	41	45	51	51
Percent Nonexperimental Patients Achieving SR-1 Year	2	5	5	5	6	6	6	6	7	10	10	10	10	16	16
Differences in Percentages	0	1	3	6	7	7	13	19	23	24	26	31	35	35	35

Percent Achieving SR-1 Year

—— Experimental Patients (N = 53)

— — — Nonexperimental Patients (N = 87)

Fig. 9. The amount of hospitalization for Group III patients prior to a significant release (SR-1 year).

134

RELEASE AND RETURN-RATE DATA

Table 9 presents the rates of release, return, success, and failure for the experimental and nonexperimental patients in flow-chart form. No statistical tests of significance were computed on these data. Column 2 of Table 9 repeats the data presented in Table 8 on the release rates of project patients. Column 3 reports the number of released patients who remained out of the hospital following their first release for at least 12 consecutive months in the community. The return rates of Column 4 are generally *higher* for the nonexperimental programs in spite of the fact that *fewer* patients were released from these programs. In the light of the discussion above, this finding suggests that the experimental program, which released more patients after less hospital treatment time, released them in better condition than those released from the nonexperimental programs.

Column 5 reports on those patients who returned to the hospital but who were subsequently re-released and achieved 12 consecutive months in the community. With the Group I patients, the Nonexperimental Units had a somewhat higher return rate. Of those Group I patients who returned, however, over half of the experimental (5/9) and nonexperimental (13/23) patients were subsequently able to leave the hospital and remain in the community for at least a year. This is one reason why the acute schizophrenic who initially returned to the hospital was not necessarily considered to represent a treatment failure. Many of these patients who returned to the hospital were initially released on their own terms. Once they had experienced failure they were able, in about 60 per cent of these instances, to achieve a significant release.

Column 6 reports the SR-1 year success rate of all patients who left the hospital. For the Group I patients *who were released*, 89 per cent (experimental) and 83 per cent (nonexperimental) were able to complete at least 12 consecutive months in the community following their first release or re-release. The patients who were never released, however, must be considered treatment failures. Column 8, therefore, reports the overall percentage of the *total* group who achieved at least 12 consecutive months in the community. The experimental program was able to achieve a significant release (SR-1 year) with 10 per cent more of its Group I, 16 per cent more of its Group II, and 35 per cent more of its Group III patients, in comparison with the nonexperimental programs.

These results suggest that the experimental program had its greatest

Table 9 - Movement of Experimental and Nonexperimental Patients into the Community

	(1) Number Completing Project (Disregarding 9 Deaths)	(2) Number Patients Obtaining a First Release	(3) Remained Out One Year After First Release	(4) Initial Return Rate of Those Released	(5) Returned But Left Again & Remained Out 1 yr	(6) Proportion of Released Patients Obtaining SR-1 year	(7) Proportion of Released Patients Failing	(8) Proportion of Total Cohort Obtaining SR-1 year
Group I — Experimental (N = 37)		35 (95%)	26 (74%)	9 (26%)	5 (14%)	31 (89%)	4 (11%)	31/37 (84%)
Schizophrenics — Nonexperimental (N = 65)		58 (89%)	35 (60%)	23 (40%)	13 (23%)	48 (83%)	10 (19%)	48/65 (74%)
Group II — Experimental (N = 29)		25 (86%)	12 (48%)	13 (52%)	3 (12%)	15 (60%)	10 (40%)	15/29 (52%)
Schizophrenics — Nonexperimental (N = 56)		34 (61%)	16 (47%)	18 (53%)	4 (12%)	20 (59%)	14 (41%)	20/56 (36%)
Group III — Experimental (N = 53)		31 (59%)	20 (65%)	11 (35%)	7 (23%)	27 (87%)	4 (13%)	27/53 (51%)
Schizophrenics — Nonexperimental (N = 87)		22 (25%)	13 (59%)	9 (41%)	1 (5%)	14 (64%)	8 (36%)	14/87 (16%)

impact with the chronically hospitalized Group III patients. This patient not only left the hospital more frequently than his nonexperimental counterpart (Column 2), but he more often obtained a significant release (SR-1 year). Of those Group III experimental patients who returned after their first release, 64 per cent (7 out of 11) were released again and obtained a significant release (SR-1 year), while only 13 per cent (1 out of 9) of the nonexperimental patients obtained a significant re-release (Columns 4 and 5). The total significant release rate for *all* Group III patients entering the project was therefore 51 per cent for the experimental, and 16 per cent for the nonexperimental programs (Column 8). This is perhaps one of the most important results of this research, since only about 5 per cent of unselected continuously hospitalized schizophrenics had been able to leave the hospital during an earlier 30-month period, let alone remain in the community for at least 12 consecutive months (SR-1 year).

The Group II patient *who was released* had a higher rate of return (Column 4) and achieved a significant second release less often (Column 5) than any other group of released patients. The Experimental Unit, while releasing more of its Group II patients, had the same proportion of returns as the Nonexperimental Units. The rate of significant release for all Group II patients, however, was 52 per cent for the Experimental Unit and 36 per cent for the Nonexperimental Unit (Column 8). As seen from Table 9, this difference was due primarily to an initially higher first-release rate of those patients from the Experimental Unit. It is also interesting to note that for the Experimental Unit, the Group II patient was able to achieve a first release more frequently than the Group III patient (86 per cent versus 59 per cent), but the rate of *significant* release for both groups was essentially the same (52 per cent *versus* 51 per cent, Column 8).

Group II patients were found to have been hospitalized an average of 75 per cent of the time during the five years preceding their being in the project. In terms of their amount of hospitalization, they are more similar to Group III patients than to Group I patients. The major difference is that the Group II patient has had some community contact, a contact followed by a return to the hospital. The Group III patient, on the other hand, had not had even the opportunity to fail in the community during the last five years. The likelihood of his remaining out of the hospital for a year following his first release was found to be greater than that of the Group II patient. This finding was totally unanticipated at the beginning of the project, although it appears, in retrospect, to have a logical explanation.

COMMUNITY STAY OUTCOME DATA

Table 10 presents the testing of statistical significance for the release and community-stay data. As can be seen in this table, the overall achievement of a one year community stay occurs significantly more frequently with the experimental program patients than with the nonexperimental groups (chi square 16.53, p < .01 for five degrees of freedom). This statistically significant finding, however, is accounted for primarily by the experimental Group III patient who achieved 12 consecutive months in the community much more frequently than his nonexperimental counterpart (51 per cent versus 16 per cent respectively).

As already seen in Table 8 at the end of Chapter 7, more of the nonexperimental Group II and Group III patients remained in the hospital during the 30-month period than did the experimental Group II and Group III patients. The chi square values for this "not released" category, then, are not repeated as part of the Table 10 calculations, since these release data have already been tested for statistical significance in Table 8. To have included this data in the calculations of the overall chi square value in Table 10 would have inflated that value and suggested a greater difference between experimental and nonexperimental programs than actually occurred with respect to the frequency of obtaining a 12-month release.

PATIENT CHARACTERISTICS
AND TYPE OF COMMUNITY PLACEMENT

At this point it becomes necessary to discuss the types of placement for those patients leaving the hospital, and the relative success of various types of placement. It has been only in recent years that the chronically hospitalized mental patient who had neither a parental, sibling, nor marital situation to return to could plan on leaving the hospital. The general philosophy had been that someone has got to take responsibility for patients who have experienced a prolonged hospitalization. Usually, the community placement of such patients depended on a social service worker's locating a relative who was willing to sign the patient out of the hospital. If there was no interested relative willing to assume this responsibility, the patient usually remained in the hospital.

Recently, the mental hospital has developed other resources for placement. The foster home program, in which foster parents are paid

Table 10 – Significance of Difference in Release and Community Stay Outcome for Experimental and Nonexperimental Program Patients

		Group I			Group II			Group III				Total
		Not Released	Released Not out 12 months	Out 12 Consec. months	Not released	Released Not out 12 months	Out 12 Consec. months	Not Released	Released Not out 12 months	Out 12 Consec. months		
Percent of Group	Experimental	5%	11%	84%	14%	34%	52%	41%	8%	51%		
	Nonexperimental	11%	15%	74%	39%	25%	36%	75%	9%	16%		
Number in Group	Experimental	2	4	31	4	10	15	22	4	27		119
	Nonexperimental	7	10	48	22	14	20	65	8	14		208
Cell Square	Experimental	(.51)	.24	.18	(3.18)	-.19	.42	(2.97)	.04	9.83		10.52
	Nonexperimental	(.30)	.14	.11	(1.83)	-.11	.24	(1.70)	.02	5.61		6.01
Contingency Sum		(.81)	.38	.29	(5.01)	-.30	.66	(4.67)	.06	15.44		16.53
Level of Significance		– –	N.S.	N.S.	– –	N.S.	N.S.	– –	N.S.	<.001		<.01

139

to take care of the ex-patient, has been used increasingly by both state and VA hospitals. The foster parent is typically paid from $125 to $175 per month for boarding and supervising the released patient. The funding of this placement comes from the patient's pension and/or social security, or from a state agency in those states that have accepted increasing responsibility for providing support for this program.

At the same time there has also been an increasing willingness on the part of the hospital staff to release the chronically hospitalized patient under those conditions in which he assumes responsibility for himself. The philosophy that the hospital must be responsible for a patient, or can relinquish this responsibility only if it is transferred to someone else, is undergoing some modification. Every mental hospital has experienced success in taking a chance on letting a chronically hospitalized patient find his own job and live by himself. It seems that for years the mental health professionals have undersold the chronically hospitalized patient in expecting too little of him, and perhaps we continue to do so.

One hospital has reported success in developing a program in which some of its chronically hospitalized patients are able to find themselves jobs and live outside the hospital on their own. At the Camarillo State Hospital, California, Wickland (1963) reports that some 10 to 15 per cent of female patients, about half of whom have been hospitalized over five years, have been able to find jobs on their own and remain in the community. These patients are given two weeks and $200 to go to the community and look for work and a place to live. They return to the hospital only if they are unable to accomplish this. From a population of 250 to 300 patients, some 40 have succeeded in this venture and there have been no serious complications. Wickland's report is not detailed enough to determine whether or not most of the successes come from those patients (30 per cent) hospitalized under one year. The decision of the hospital, however, to let a patient determine for herself when and how she wants to leave the hospital, represents a significant shift in the philosophy of patient rehabilitation. If a patient handles her hospital work assignment and interpersonal relationships adequately, she is allowed to set her own date for an attempt at community living. Several patients have reportedly shown unusual resourcefulness in obtaining the necessary $200 for initial expenses. At first, none of the patients apparently believed the hospital staff were serious in their proposal, and participated reluctantly in discussing plans to leave the hospital. After some months there was a waiting list of patients who wanted to take part in these discussions and planning groups. It seems that the social climate of the ward had indeed undergone considerable change, and that patients were responding positively to the expectation of the staff that they were capable of leaving the hospital and successfully assuming responsibility for themselves.

In the present study, both the experimental and nonexperimental patients left the hospital to live in a wide variety of community situations. As seen in Table 11, there were significant overall differences in the placement of Group I, II, and III patients (chi square 56.39, p. < .001 for ten degrees of freedom). The Group I patient returned more often to live with his wife than did the Group II or Group III patient. The Group III patient returned less often to live with parents, but was placed in a foster home more often than either Group I and Group II patients. In general, the Group III patient was more likely to find that his relatives had closed ranks and organized their lives without him. It is extremely difficult for the relatives of many long-term patients to respond to suggestions that they visit or even write the patient, let alone make arrangements for him to live with them. The Group III patient, therefore, was usually placed with nonrelatives.

It was surprising that the Group III patient went to live on his own as often as he did. There were no significant differences in the extent to which the chronic patient was able to live under these circumstances as compared with the acute or semi-chronic patient. Neither were there any significant differences between groups in the utilization of a supervised boarding situation (Domiciliary or Member Employee), although this placement tended to be used least frequently by the acute patient.

In the VA Domiciliary, the patient must assume a large share of the responsibility for himself in accepting an assignment, getting to meals, taking medication, going on passes, and the like. In exchange for his assuming this level of responsibility and productivity, board, room, and recreational activities are provided for him. The VA Member-Employee program is one in which the patient performs a regular job in the hospital. In return, he receives board and room and earns a small amount of money. Although often requiring a higher level of assumed responsibility and independence than Domiciliary living, it is nevertheless a semi-protective placement.

The patient's level of behavioral adjustment was found to be related to the kind of community situation he entered. For example, it was found that the poorly adjusted patient would often be accepted as a foster home placement, but was rarely allowed to live on his own. The patients' behavioral ratings at the time of release were examined and the following differences were found: 1) Those patients who left the hospital to live "on their own" had an average behavioral adjustment rating of 74.5 (90th percentile) at the time of their release; 2) those patients returning to their wives had an average behavioral

Table 11 - Community Placement of all Group I, II, and III Patients

		Parents	Wife	Other Relatives	On Own or School	Supervised Boarding	Foster Home	N
Percent of Group	Group I	38%	15%	17%	22%	8%	1%	93
	Group II	41%	2%	13%	20%	20%	3%	59
	Group III	15%	4%	8%	26%	19%	28%	53
Number in Group	Group I	35	14	16	20	7	1	93
	Group II	24	1	8	12	12	2	59
	Group III	8	2	4	14	10	15	53
Cell Square Contingency	Group I	.70	5.15	.86	.04	2.91	6.32	15.98
	Group II	1.14	3.10	.00	.11	1.65	1.97	7.97
	Group III	5.00	1.31	1.42	.37	.83	23.51	32.44
	Sum	6.84	9.56	2.28	.52	5.39	31.80	56.39
Level of Significance		$<.05$	$<.01$	N.S.	N.S.	N.S.	$<.001$	$<.001$

rating of 73.7 (88th percentile); 3) those patients who left to live in a setting which demanded responsibility and initiative on their part (Member-Employee and Domiciliary) had a rating of 70.8 (79th percentile); 4) those going to live with brothers, sisters, or other relatives, had a rating of 69.2 (75th percentile); 5) those going to live with their parents had a rating of 68.1 (70th percentile); and 6) those who entered a foster home had an exit behavioral adjustment rating of 60.0 (50th percentile).

Relatively few patients who went to non-foster-home settings were below average in behavioral adjustment at the time of their exit from the hospital. Of the 95 patients going to parents, sisters, brothers, or other relatives, 18 (19 per cent) were poorly adjusted (below the 50th percentile), while 3 of the 29 (10 per cent) patients going to Domiciliary and Member-Employee programs were poorly adjusted. Only 1 of the 46 (2 per cent) patients going "on their own" was poorly adjusted, while none of the 17 patients returning to their wives was poorly adjusted. In contrast, patients who entered the foster home were very different from those who entered other community settings, with 49 per cent of them being rated below average in behavioral adjustment at the time of their release from the hospital. It seemed that almost any patient who had sufficient funds and who was not a danger to himself or others was eligible for a foster home placement. In many ways, the foster home appeared to be a miniature hospital setting since the average behavioral adjustment level of patients who remained in the hospital or went to a foster home was found to be about the same.

Both the adjustment level of the patient and the length of his hospitalization, then, appeared to be related to the type of placement open to him. The long-term patient was most likely to enter a non-relative setting. If he was rated as poorly adjusted at exit, this setting was most likely to be a foster home. On the other hand, one could not have predicted the setting to which a well-adjusted patient went, for the range of possible settings open to him was usually much greater.

SUCCESSFUL AND UNSUCCESSFUL COMMUNITY PLACEMENT

If one judges the success of a community placement only in terms of whether or not a patient remained out, the foster home placement was quite successful. If one judges the success of a community placement in terms of the extent to which the patient showed an improvement in his social-behavioral adjustment between the 3rd and 12th post-hospital month, then the foster home placement was singularly unsuccessful, as will be seen.

The prediction of return to the hospital is found to be extremely difficult (Marks et al., 1963 and Freeman and Simmons, 1963). Using data at exit, neither of these studies found that the patient's ability to remain in the community could be predicted with any accuracy. The only variable that barely reached significance in the Marks study (ibid., p. 123), was the activity therapist's rating of the patient's behavioral adjustment prior to exit. This relationship between the evaluation of behavioral adjustment and subsequent return to the hospital was also reported (phi coefficient .14) by Pishkin and Bradshaw (1960). In this study, they also found that the number of previous trial visits (phi coefficient .27) and years of current hospitalization (phi coefficient .29) were predictive of return to the hospital. In the present study, the Group II patient who had been in and out of the hospital during the last five years had a somewhat higher return rate from a first release than did the Group I or Group III patient (see Table 9). In this sense, then, our data tend to support the Pishkin and Bradshaw (ibid.) finding regarding the relationship between number of previous trial visits and return to the hospital. Our data, however, do not support their finding that the patient with the most years of current hospitalization tends to return more frequently to the hospital, for the Group III chronically hospitalized patients returned to the hospital at about the same rate as did the acute Group I patients, and less often than the semi-chronic Group II patients (Table 9).

Although data gathered at exit do not predict return to the hospital, data gathered in the community shortly after the patient leaves the hospital were found to be predictive of return to the hospital. In our study, for example, the patient who had remained out of the hospital for three months and had obtained full-time employment had a 95 per cent chance of remaining in the community for the rest of the year. The patient who was unemployed or employed part time at three months, however, had a 75 per cent chance of achieving an SR-1 year (phi coefficient between employment and community stay equal .26, significant beyond the .01 level). Freeman and Simmons (1963) reported a correlation of .23 for male patients who remained out of the hospital, and their regularity of work performance. In our study, the social adjustment rating (Appendix C) at three months was also found to correlate .22 (phi coefficient) with return to the hospital. If the veteran was rated above average in his community adjustment at three months, his chance of achieving an SR-1 year was 91 per cent, while 74 per cent of those rated below average remained out during the rest of the year.

In general, at this point, the problem of predicting, at exit, the patient's return to the hospital must be regarded as unsolved. From data describing his initial community adjustment, the prediction of return to the hospital is somewhat better, but still far from adequate. Freeman and Simmons (ibid.) suggest that rehabilitation is actually a two-stage process; (1) successful community tenure, and (2) performance during the patient's stay in the community. Since we obtained two ratings of community adjustment following release, one at 3 months and one at 12 months (see Appendix C), we were able to determine the degree of improvement or regression in adjustment between the third and twelfth months.

As mentioned previously, we determined the whereabouts and employment record of 100 per cent of the SR-1 year patients. We obtained ratings of social and psychiatric adjustment (items 3 to 9) on 97 per cent of the SR-1 year patients. If the adjustment rating at 12 months showed a drop in community adjustment as compared with the 3-month rating, the patient was regarded as showing a regression in his adjustment. These data allowed us to determine which community settings were poor outcome situations in that they either: (1) failed to keep the patient from returning to the hospital during a 12-consecutive-months period, or (2) showed the patient as regressing in his community adjustment between the 3-month and 12-month rating of adjustment in his community setting.

As seen in Table 12, the success or failure rate varied significantly in terms of the type of placement used (chi square 43.31, p. < .001 for 10 degrees of freedom). The patient who left the hospital on his own both remained out for 12 months and also maintained his level of social adjustment more frequently than expected. The veteran who went to a supervised living placement (Domiciliary or Member-Employee) failed to remain out for 12 months as often as expected. And finally, the foster home placement led to a much higher rate of adjustment regression than expected, but had a very low return rate. Not only did the foster home patient enter the community with the lowest behavioral adjustment at exit, but he was even more poorly adjusted 12 months after leaving the hospital than he had been at 3 months.

In short, the patient who went to live with any relative had a community outcome that did not deviate from expected. The poorest outcome placement among relatives was the parental one. Patients who went to live on their own had the best outcome. Patients who were placed in a supervised living arrangement had a higher-than-expected

Table 12 - Return, Regression, and Success Rates for Various Community Placements
(arranged in order of overall success rate)

		Failed to remain out 12 months	Out 12 months but regressed social adjustment	Out 12 months maintained or improved social adjustment	Total	Level of Significance
Number and Percent of Group	On own	2 (4%)	9 (20%)	35 (76%)	46	
	Wife	3 (18%)	4 (24%)	10 (59%)	17	
	Other relatives	6 (21%)	10 (36%)	12 (43%)	28	
	Supervised Living	13 (33%)	5 (17%)	11 (38%)	29	
	Parents	23 (34%)	21 (31%)	23 (34%)	67	
	Foster Home	3 (17%)	12 (67%)	3 (17%)	18	
	Total and Average Percent	50 (24%)	61 (30%)	94 (46%)	205	
Cell Square Contingency	On own	7.56	1.61	9.16	18.33	$<.001$
	Wife	.30	.24	.62	1.16	N.S.
	Other relatives	.01	.35	.01	.37	N.S.
	Supervised living	4.90	1.51	.40	6.81	$<.05$
	Parents	2.75	.06	1.93	4.74	N.S.
	Foster Home	.45	8.07	3.38	11.90	$<.01$
	Sum	15.97	11.84	15.50	43.31	$<.001$

146

return rate. Patients who went to foster homes had a low return rate, but a high rate of adjustment regression. This setting perhaps expects the least from patients initially, and accepts the greatest amount of behavioral regression without returning the patient to the hospital. In general, the failure of the patient to remain in the community appears to be more a function of the setting's tolerance and less a function of the patient's subsequent improvement or regression in the setting. This may in large part explain why prediction of return to the hospital has proven so difficult.

These results have another implication as well, namely, that the incidence of regression in community adjustment occurs most frequently in those settings that appear to accept a low level of patients' behavioral adjustment. When little is expected of the released patient, such as in the foster home setting, he may respond to this expectation by a drop in adjustment level. Once his needs are taken care of and he can remain relatively passive in meeting the minimal demands of a foster home situation, he is most apt to show a behavioral regression (see Stotsky, 1966, for further evidence of this). The foster home parents are paid to care for the patient and are likely to keep him unless he engages in antisocial or acting-out behavior. The foster home program, then, often seemed nontherapeutic. Had these foster homes expected a high level of responsibility on the part of the patient and enabled him to function more independently, the outcome of our hospital's foster home placements might have been better.

Patients who went to live on their own usually had full-time jobs and, in addition, had to care for their own personal needs. This situation clearly demands a great deal of responsibility and initiative from the patient. Perhaps it is this demand for responsible behavior that leads to the maintenance or improvement in one's community adjustment. Although this hypothesis can neither be proven nor disproven in this study, the evidence would seem to support the conclusion of Freeman and Simmons (1963, pp. 147–148) who suggest that the patient performs best in the setting that imposes the highest demands.

TYPES OF COMMUNITY PLACEMENT OF EXPERIMENTAL AND NONEXPERIMENTAL PATIENTS

The experimental program, which released significantly more of its Group II and Group III patients (SR-1 year) than did the nonexperimental program, could have accomplished this simply by using pro-

Table 13 - Type of Community Placement for Experimental and Nonexperimental Patients

		On Own	Wife	Other Relatives	Supervised Living	Parents	Foster Home	Sum
Percent Placed	Experimental	30%	8%	11%	14%	24%	13%	
	Nonexperimental	17%	9%	16%	14%	39%	6%	
Number Placed	Experimental	27	7	10	13	22	12	91
	Nonexperimental	19	10	18	16	45	6	114
Cell Square Contingency	Experimental	2.14	.03	.46	.00	2.00	2.00	6.63
	Nonexperimental	1.70	.03	.37	.00	1.59	1.60	5.29
	Sum	3.84	.06	.83	.00	3.59	3.60	11.92
Level of Significance		<.05	N.S.	N.S.	N.S.	N.S.	N.S.	<.05

tective situations that did not demand a great deal of the patient. Had this occurred, the significant differences in community placement between the experimental and nonexperimental programs would not have been so much a measure of program effectiveness as it would have been a measure of staff ingenuity and persistence.

As can be seen in Table 13, there was a significant difference between the experimental program and the nonexperimental program with regard to the initial placement of all patients (chi square 11.92, p. < .05 for five degrees of freedom). The experimental patients were more likely to be placed on their own than were the nonexperimental patients (30 versus 17 per cent). Also, somewhat more (not significant) of the experimental patients were placed in foster homes than were the nonexperimental patients (13 per cent versus 6 per cent). On the other hand, somewhat more of the nonexperimental patients went with parents than experimental patients (39 versus 24 per cent). In general, however, the differences in placement frequencies were small and could hardly have accounted for the higher release rates of the experimental program patients. The low exit adjustment of the foster home placements is counterbalanced by the high adjustment level required for patients going on their own. Thus neither program disproportionately used the types of placements that would have allowed them to place behaviorally regressed patients.

COMMUNITY SOCIAL ADJUSTMENT OF EXPERIMENTAL AND NONEXPERIMENTAL PATIENTS

Each of the 327 patients entering the project was followed over a 30-month period. During this time, 205 of these patients were released from the hospital. If a patient remained out of the hospital for one consecutive year and maintained or improved his social adjustment between the 3rd- and 12th-month rating, he was regarded as an adjustment success. If, on the other hand, the patient either failed to remain in the community for one year or showed regression in his social adjustment, he was regarded as an adjustment failure.

In order to determine whether or not the experimental program patients achieved a successful adjustment more frequently than their non-experimental counterparts, the frequencies of adjustment successes and failures were tabulated for each group of patients. To test these frequencies for statistical significance, the Cell Square Contingency method was used. As discussed earlier, the total sample of 327 patients was maintained since the proportions of experimental and nonexperimental patients in Groups I, II, and III were almost identical. Had less than the total group been used to test the contingencies, these proportions would have been destroyed. As a result, the overall chi square value would reflect both the differences in group proportions as well as the outcome frequencies.

If one were to report an overall chi square that included the contingency values for the frequencies of patients not released, one would unnecessarily inflate the overall chi square value. Whether or not a patient was released from the hospital is not an issue at this point. Because of this, the chi square value is obtained from only the contingencies arising out of the "returned or regressed" and "maintained or improved" cells. In this way, the differences in effectiveness of the experimental and nonexperimental programs with respect to their relative impact on community social adjustment can be tested. The contingency values are added only if the outcome of the experimental program exceeds that of the nonexperimental program. If the outcome is reversed, the contingency value for the cell is subtracted from the total chi square. A significant positive chi square value, therefore, indicates that the experimental program patients had a better overall outcome than the nonexperimental patients.

As seen in Table 14, the community social adjustment outcome was significantly better for the experimental than for the nonexperimental patients (chi square 19.11, p. < .01 for five degrees of freedom). These results, however, occurred primarily because of the effect of the experimental program on the chronic Group III patients. Somewhat more of the experimental Group II patients maintained or improved their social adjustment between the 3rd and 12th post-hospital month, as compared with their nonexperimental counterparts (31 versus 16 per cent). This difference, however, did not reach statistical significance. In this analysis, a failure in social community adjustment is regarded as either a failure to remain in the community for one year, or a regression in social adjustment during that time. As seen earlier in Table 12, a regression in social adjustment does not necessarily lead to rehospitalization if the situation (such as the foster home placement) is highly tolerant of behavioral regression. A successful social-adjustment outcome, then, occurs when the patient remains out of the hospital for at least 12 consecutive months, and also maintains or improves his adjustment during this time. The experimental program had its greatest differential impact on the more chronically hospitalized schizophrenic patient with respect to social-adjustment outcome, a finding consistent with the release data reported earlier.

Table 14 - Community Social Adjustment Outcome for Experimental and Nonexperimental Patients*

		Group I-Social Adjustment			Group II-Social Adjustment			Group III-Social Adjustment			Total
		Not Released	Returned or Regressed	Maintained or Improved	Not Released	Returned or Regressed	Maintained or Improved	Not Released	Returned or Regressed	Maintained or Improved	
Percent of Group	Experimental	5%	46%	49%	14%	55%	31%	42%	21%	38%	
	Nonexperimental	11%	40%	49%	39%	45%	16%	75%	18%	7%	
Number in Group	Experimental	2	17	18	4	16	9	22	11	20	119
	Nonexperimental	7	26	32	22	25	9	65	16	6	208
Cell Square Contingency	Experimental	(.51)	-.13	.00	(3.18)	-.08	.87	(2.97)	-.15	11.61	12.12
	Nonexperimental	(.30)	-.07	.00	(1.83)	-.05	.51	(1.70)	-.08	6.68	6.99
	Sum	(.81)	-.20	.00	(5.01)	-.13	1.38	(4.67)	-.23	18.29	19.11
Level of Significance		- -	N.S.	N.S.	- -	N.S.	N. S	- -	N.S.	$< .001$	$< .01$

* The five patients for whom there was missing data were included by prorating their outcome in terms of the outcome
for their group and program.

151

WORK ADJUSTMENT OF EXPERIMENTAL AND NONEXPERIMENTAL PATIENTS

Item 2 of the Follow-up Questionnaire (Appendix C) asks the informant whether or not the veteran is employed full time, part time, or is unemployed. Unlike the other items on the questionnaire that are more subjective in nature, the work item was found to be much more objectively rated. Some patients on trial visit were seen personally by a social worker at three months after the patient left the hospital. For a group of 25 such patients, a social worker independently rated the patient's adjustment on the follow-up questionnaire. These ratings were compared with the ratings of the community informant. A product moment correlation of .90 was found between the social worker's ratings of work adjustment and the informant's rating of this same area. Less consistency was found in the social-worker and family ratings of social adjustment. This is why, in the preceding section, change scores were used rather than absolute scores indicating the level of social adjustment. Some informants were quite biased in their ratings; for example, the written comments on an enclosed letter would often contradict the actual ratings that had been made on items 3 to 9. At times, a parent would rate the veteran as adjusting well, socializing, and the like, and in his letter would indicate that the veteran was "doing so poorly" at home that he was planning to rehospitalize him. The unreliability of these ratings, then, undoubtedly stems from their asking for a global evaluation of adjustment rather than asking for specific and concrete behavioral ratings.

In the original study by Fairweather et al. (1960), the only item that was sensitive to differences in treatment effectiveness was the employment item. It is this writer's opinion that the employment criterion is perhaps one of the best operational measures of how well the patient is meeting one of the important expectations of society.

From the data in Table 15, it appears that significantly more of all groups of experimental patients were rated at the 12th month as being employed full time than were those treated on the nonexperimental programs (chi square 19.48, p. < .01 for five degrees of freedom). Patients who were not included as working full time were those who (1) had full-time hospital jobs (Member-Employee programs), (2) were going to school full time, and (3) worked on a family farm. Only patients who worked full time for someone outside the family for salary or wages were included in this category. The only "negative" results of the experimental program with respect to employment outcome was the higher proportion of Group III experimental patients in the community

Table 15 - Work Adjustment Outcome* for Experimental and Nonexperimental Patients

		GROUP I			GROUP II			GROUP III			Total
		Not Out 12 Months	Out 12 months		Not Out 12 Months	Out 12 months		Not Out 12 Months	Out 12 months		
			Not working Full Time	Working Full Time		Not working Full Time	Working Full Time		Not working Full Time	Working Full Time	
Percent of Group	Experimental	16%	49%	35%	48%	28%	24%	49%	32%	19%	
	Nonexperimental	26%	60%	14%	64%	30%	5%	84%	15%	1%	
Number in Group	Experimental	6	18	13	14	8	7	26	17	10	119
	Nonexperimental	17	39	9	36	17	3	73	13	1	208
Cell Square Contingency	Experimental	(.69)	.35	3.13	(.97)	.13	3.21	(2.78)	-3.41	9.00	12.41
	Nonexperimental	(.39)	.20	1.79	(.55)	.08	1.81	(1.59)	-1.95	5.14	7.07
	Sum	- -	.55	4.92	- -	.21	5.02	- -	-5.36	14.14	19.48
Level of Significance		- -	N.S.	<.05	- -	N.S.	.05	- -	<.05	<.001	<.01

*Post-hospital work adjustment is generally lower for veteran than nonveteran psychiatric patients, probably because of the pension given to service-connected veterans as long as they remain unemployed.

153

not working full time at 12 months. The proportion of this group out and working, however, more than compensates for this negative result. In a clinical sense, a chronic patient who remains out for one full year cannot be regarded as a failure even though he is not working full time. The outcome criteria of Table 15, however, is that of "being out 12 months *and* working full time."

Although not presented, the employment-outcome differences between programs at 3 months were also statistically significant (chi square 13.01, p. < .05 for five degrees of freedom), and favored the experimental program patients. As seen in Table 15, these differences became even clearer at the 12th-month rating (chi square 19.48). What happened was that those who left the experimental program and who were employed full time at 3 months, usually remained out and employed for 12 months. Other experimental patients who had been working only part time at 3 months were found to be working full time at the 12th month. Some of the employed nonexperimental patients, on the other hand, had returned to the hospital by the 12th month, or had stopped working full time.

Why the experimental program had such a differential effect on the post-hospital employment of the patient is not entirely clear. Our aides were very helpful to patients in providing job leads. One aide allowed two patients to live with him until they earned their first pay check. Another aide boarded at his home a chronic patient who worked at a nearby restaurant, and helped him establish social ties with the community. In part, also, it may have been related to the reinforcement of the patient's earning his increased levels of freedom while in the hospital, a characteristic of the experimental program. As already mentioned at the beginning of Chapter 5, the attendance of the experimental patients at scheduled activities was somewhat higher than the attendance of the nonexperimental patients at these activities. The experimental patient was expected to be responsible for meeting the requirements of his ward level, and received privileges only in exchange for responsible behavior.

This writer believes that the best explanation of the differences in work adjustment between the experimental and the nonexperimental patients is that we successfully communicated to patients our expectancy that they were to obtain jobs. Once the patient reached the discharge ward, he found himself in a climate of planning for discharge, a climate he was expected to participate in. Other patients were going to town looking for jobs, and it was expected that almost everyone should seek work if at all possible. If a patient wanted to explore the possibility of living in a situation that did not demand work (such as living with relatives), he had to write his own letters. If there was an indication of covert rejection of the patient by the family, the staff would often say to the patient, "Your family doesn't want you. They haven't even answered your letter." The staff, then, was not in the position of negotiating the return of the patient to the family home, but usually left it up to the family and the patient to work out mutually acceptable plans. This undoubtedly accounts for the less frequent placement of the experimental patient with his parents (Table 13). If the patient had to make other plans for leaving the hospital, in lieu of returning to his parents, one of the alternatives open to him was to find himself a job. This staff expectation for the patient's working, communicated by the manner in which the experimental staff handled discharge planning with the patient, helped many patients to assume the responsibility not only for finding work, but also for keeping their jobs once they became employed.

The kinds of jobs open to the chronically hospitalized patient were generally quite different from those open to the acute patient. Of the 10 experimental Group III patients employed full time at the 12-month follow-up, two worked in laundries, two in construction, and two on farms. The remaining four worked in a cafe, a bakery, an animal hospital, and a garage. Some of the experimental Group I and Group II patients also obtained jobs in restaurants. Most restaurants ordinarily had a high turnover of dishwashers and bus boys. They were often willing to take the risk of giving a job to an ex-mental patient looking for work. Some were found to be so stable and dependable that later, others were hired.

SIX YEAR FOLLOW-UP OF EXPERIMENTAL AND NONEXPERIMENTAL PATIENTS

The Experimental program began March 1, 1959 and remained in full operation for the next 30 months, or until September 1961. Although the program actually continued to function until July 1962, the vast majority of patients had left the hospital by July of 1961. A primary focus during the last year of the program was that of completing the data collection and analysis. In effect, then, the program had had its major impact on patient rehabilitation by July 1961.

During July, 1967, the author contacted the psychology and social work staff * of the Fort Meade Hospital regarding a possible follow-up

* The author is indebted to George B. Kish and Clifford Cook of Psychology Service, and Don Hartford and Pat Bachand of Social Work Service, for their assistance in providing the follow-up data on project patients.

of the 327 project patients. Two major questions could be answered by such a follow-up study: First, one wonders whether or not the hospital staff continued to work toward discharge with those chronic and semi-chronic patients who still remained in the hospital at the end of the project period. Or, once the stimulus provided by the research project was withdrawn, did the staff accept a status quo for these remaining chronically hospitalized patients? Secondly, one wonders whether or not a measurable difference in treatment outcome between the experimental and nonexperimental programs could be detected some six years after the project was over. Although statistically significant treatment differences between experimental and nonexperimental programs were clearly evident during the project and up to one year after release, treatment effect differences may well have disappeared after the one year follow-up (see Fairweather and Simon, 1963, for example).

The staff at the Fort Meade hospital agreed to provide information about current whereabouts and release status for all experimental and nonexperimental project patients. During July, 1967, the names of all 327 project patients were sent to the Fort Meade Hospital. Information about four categories of current status was requested, namely: alive or dead, currently hospitalized or released, trial visit or discharge status, and foster home or non-foster home placement.

A survey of current whereabouts and release status has one advantage over other follow-up information in that it is easily obtainable. It does not, however, constitute adequate information about post-hospital social and work adjustment. Also, some patients, currently recorded as discharged from the Fort Meade Hospital, have certainly been hospitalized elsewhere. Other sources of information allow one to make a very close estimate of the frequency of rehospitalization elsewhere. For example, during the project, between seven and eight out of every 100 patients released from the Fort Meade Hospital were actually hospitalized elsewhere. In another study of chronically hospitalized patients transferred to 11 different VA hospitals, 31 or 15 per cent of 201 released patients were hospitalized elsewhere at the end of an eight year follow-up period (Gurel, 1966a). The lower rehospitalization-elsewhere rate for Fort Meade patients (7–8 per cent) is probably accounted for by the fact that there are few alternative psychiatric facilities available to the ex-Fort Meade patient. If he needs further hospitalization he is likely to return to Fort Meade to receive it. The data from these two sources allow one to make a rather exact estimate regarding the probability of patients being currently rehospitalized elsewhere. For purposes of this present survey, the estimate is set at 10 per cent, slightly higher than that typical of the Fort Meade patient, but slightly lower than that reported by Gurel (*ibid.*).

RELEASE STATUS OF FORT MEADE PATIENTS AT THE SIX YEAR FOLLOW-UP. At the end of the 30-month project, 75 per cent of Group I, 42 per cent of Group II, and 31 per cent of Group III patients were living in the community. Six years later, the per cent of patients living in the community (corrected for estimated rehospitalization elsewhere) was 80 per cent for Group I, 73 per cent for Group II, and 71 per cent for Group III patients. In other words, approximately twice as many Group II and Group III patients were living in the community six years after the project was over than was the case at the end of the study. It seems clear, then, that the staff of the Fort Meade hospital succeeded in providing community status for a very high per cent of their chronic and semi-chronic patients.

How do these release data compare with those found in other studies? The familiar 6–7 per cent release rate for schizophrenic patients hospitalized beyond two years (Brown, 1960) appears to represent a gross underestimation of current release rates for chronically hospitalized patients. Gurel (1966a), for example, found that 40.2 per cent of chronically hospitalized schizophrenic patients transferred to 11 different VA hospitals were living in the community eight years after transfer. Of those released, 26 per cent had been placed in nursing or foster homes. Seventy-two per cent of Group II and Group III Fort Meade patients achieved the status of community living (corrected for rehospitalization) some eight and one half years after entering the project, with 46 per cent of those in the community living in foster homes. This represents an impressive achievement for the Fort Meade staff.

EXPERIMENTAL AND NONEXPERIMENTAL PATIENTS SIX YEARS LATER. The question remains of whether or not there is a measurable outcome difference between experimental and nonexperimental patients six years after the end of the project. First of all, no differences were found in the frequency with which a foster home placement was used for the experimental versus the nonexperimental patient groups. Foster home placements were used more often for the chronic groups of experimental and nonexperimental patients. Of those in the community as of July 1967, 13 per cent of Group I, 21 per cent of Group II, and 51 per cent of Group III experimental and nonexperimental patients were in foster homes.

Differences were found, however, in the current release status of experimental and nonexperimental patients. Three categories of release status were examined: (1) currently hospitalized, (2) on trial visit, (3) discharged. Trial visit status typically represents the patient who has not yet completed one year out of the hospital. Between 94 and 96 per cent of all Group II and III Fort Meade patients initially entered the community on trial visit status, and achieved discharge status only if they remained out of the hospital for one year. As of July 1967, then, trial visit status typically represented a recent hospitalization at Fort Meade. Although trial visit indicates a current hospital release, it represents a lower level of release achievement than discharge status.

Table 16 presents the release status * of experimental and nonexperimental patients six years after the program was over. As seen in Table 16, there is an overall higher proportion of experimental patients on discharge status, and a higher proportion of nonexperimental patients on trial visit and currently hospitalized status. The most striking differences, however, are found with the Group III patients. Of this group, 81 per cent of experimental and 49 per cent of nonexperimental patients are on discharge status. The percentage of the nonexperimental patients who are currently hospitalized or on trial visit is higher than that found with the experimental Group III patients (26 per cent versus 11 per cent, and 25 per cent versus 8 per cent respectively). Thus, six years after the end of the project, a measurable treatment effect difference between the experimental and nonexperimental programs was found, especially with respect to current release status of Group III patients. As a matter of fact, the release status differences in the Group III patients could have arisen by chance less than once in one hundred times (Group III chi square value 12.86, p. < .01 for 2 degrees of freedom).

OVERALL REHABILITATION OUTCOME
FOR ALL 327 EXPERIMENTAL
AND NONEXPERIMENTAL
SCHIZOPHRENIC PATIENTS

One of the unique features of this study was that the patients who were included as subjects represented an unselected group of nongeriatric male schizophrenic veterans. The group included patients who were

* It must be remembered that release status represents only one estimate of treatment outcome. Nothing is known about the current level of post-hospital social and employment adjustment, areas in which the experimental patients were typically better adjusted than their nonexperimental counterparts on the one year follow-up.

Table 16 - Six Year Follow-up on Release Status of Experimental and Nonexperimental Patients.

		Group I			Group II			Group III			Total
		In Hospital	Trial Visit	Discharged	In Hospital	Trial Visit	Discharged	In Hospital	Trial Visit	Discharged	Total
Percent of Group	Experimental	8%	8%	83%	25%	11%	64%	11%	8%	81%	
	Nonexperimental	13%	9%	78%	16%	20%	63%	26%	25%	49%	
Number of Group	Experimental	3	3	30	7	3	18	5	4	38	111*
	Nonexperimental	8	6	50	8	10	31	22	21	41	197*
Cell Square Contingency	Experimental	.25	- -	.05	-.47	.61	- -	2.28	2.78	3.17	8.67
	Nonexperimental	.14	- -	.03	-.27	.35	- -	1.28	1.56	1.79	4.88
	Sum	.39	- -	.08	-.74	.96	- -	3.56	4.34	4.96	13.55
Level of Significance		N.S.	N.S.	N.S.	N.S.	N.S.	N.S.	<.10	<.05	<.05	<.10

*Eight experimental and 11 nonexperimental patients had died between the end of the project and July 1967.

159

acute and chronic, newly admitted and chronically regressed, privileged open ward, nonprivileged locked ward, and so on. Many rehabilitation studies are highly selective in that their patient sample included some who could initially handle an open-ward setting and who were selectively referred to that particular treatment program from other wards. An example would be the Fairweather study (1964) in which the patient sample was composed of only those patients who were referred, who agreed to a transfer, and who were accepted by the research staff. This patient sample included only a very small per cent of patients from closed wards. In addition, the analysis of rehabilitation outcome did not include those who were sent back to locked wards or who left the hospital without permission (*ibid.*, p. 157). Although the study cited above did have an adequate control group and could thus measure the differential effects of its experimental program, the restrictions imposed by the *range* of patients studied does not allow one to evaluate its rehabilitation potential for an unselected group of hospitalized schizophrenic patients. (For a discussion of the selectivity problem, and the consequent low generalizability of results for the Fairweather program, see Mac Donald, 1966.) It is of considerable interest, therefore, to summarize the overall results in terms of all 327 nongeriatric schizophrenic male veterans who completed the study.

Seven possible outcomes have been examined and tested for statistical significance with respect to the rehabilitation effects of the experimental and nonexperimental programs. These findings are summarized in Table 17. In general, the in-hospital differences (behavioral adjustment, days hospitalized, and release rates) clearly favored the experimental program patients and could have arisen by chance less than once in one thousand times (p. < .001). The one year follow-up differences (12 consecutive months in the community, and social and employment adjustment at that time) again clearly favored the experimental program patients, and could have arisen by chance less than once in one hundred times (p. < .01). The six year follow-up release status differences, although still favoring the experimental program patients, could have arisen once in ten times by chance.

The experimental program clearly affected the more chronically hospitalized patient to a greater extent than his nonexperimental counterpart. As seen in Table 17, only two of the seven outcome criteria differences clearly favored the experimental Group I patient (in-hospital behavioral adjustment and employment adjustment one year after release). With respect to the semi-chronic Group II patient, the experimental program affected him to a statistically significant extent on two of the seven outcome measures (in-hospital behavioral adjustment and

Table 17 - Overall Treatment Outcome Results of Experimental and Nonexperimental Patients

Source of Information		Level of Behavioral Adjustment	Median Days Hospitalized	Released Versus Not Released	Achieved 12 Months in Community	Good Social Adjustment Outcome	Good Work Adjustment Outcome	Discharge Status Six Years Later
Probability of No Difference Between Experimental and Nonexperimental Programs		$p < .001$	$p < .001$	$p < .001$	$p < .01$	$p < .01$	$p < .01$	$p < .10$
Source of Information		Table 6 Fig. 2 & 3	Table 7	Table 8	Table 10	Table 14	Table 15	Table 16
Group I	Experimental	86 %tile	238	95%	84%	49%	35%	83%
	Nonexperimental	71 %tile	285	89%	74%	48%	14%	78%
	Significance	$p < .02$	N.S.	N.S.	N.S.	N.S.	$p < .05$	N.S.
Group II	Experimental	89 %tile	609	86%	52%	31%	24%	64%
	Nonexperimental	48 %tile	836	61%	36%	16%	5%	63%
	Significance	$p < .001$	$p < .10$	$p < .10$	N.S.	N.S.	$p < .05$	N.S.
Group III	Experimental	70 %tile	789	59%	51%	38%	19%	81%
	Nonexperimental	30 %tile	915+	25%	16%	7%	1%	49%
	Significance	$p < .001$	$p < .001$	$p < .001$	$p < .001$	$p < .001$	$p < .001$	$p < .05$

one year employment adjustment). In addition, two other outcome measures favored, but did not quite reach statistical significance at the .05 level, the experimental program Group II patient (length of hospitalization and release rate differences).

The chronically hospitalized Group III experimental patients had a significantly better treatment outcome on all seven outcome measures than did the nonexperimental Group III patients. For example, the experimental Group III patient, in contrast to his nonexperimental counterpart: 1) developed a higher level of in-hospital behavioral adjustment, 2) spent less time in the hospital during the project, 3) left the hospital more frequently, 4) achieved 12 consecutive months in the community more often, had a better 5) social, and 6) work adjustment one year after release, and 7) was found to be on discharge status more frequently six years later.

In general, the rehabilitation differences between the experimental and nonexperimental programs were greatest for the chronic Group III schizophrenic, and least for the acute Group I schizophrenic patient group. Even with the acute group, however, if the criterion of success is one in which the patient must remain out for at least 12 consecutive months and be found working full time at the 12-month follow-up, then significantly more of the experimental program Group I patients reached this level of adjustment than did the nonexperimental program Group I patients. It is also of interest to compare the outcome of the experimental Group III chronic patients (presumably poor risks) with the nonexperimental Group I acute patients (presumably good risks). Again, if one sets a criterion of working full time after 12 consecutive months out of the hospital, the experimental chronic Group III patients do as well as the acute nonexperimental Group I patients.

SUMMARY

Of the 336 experimental and nonexperimental patients in the project, nine died, 122 remained hospitalized, 205 reached the community, and 155 achieved a significant release (i.e., a release followed by 12 consecutive months in the community). Even though a smaller proportion of the nonexperimental patients reached the community during the 30-month project, their initial return rate to the hospital was found to be somewhat higher (although not statistically different from) the initial return rate for the experimental patients. The differences in significant release rates (SR-1 year) between the experimental and nonexperimental programs were found to be greatest for the more chronically hospitalized patients, a finding that suggests that the experimental program had its greatest differential impact on the more chronic schizophrenic groups. This conclusion is supported from other outcome data as well.

An examination of the relationship between the types of community placement used and the adjustment levels of patients who entered them revealed that patients who lived in the community "on their own" or "with wife" were better adjusted at the time of release than patients who went to foster homes. As might be expected also, the use of various types of community placement differed for the three groups of schizophrenic patients, with the acute patients more often returning to live with relatives and the chronic patients more often being placed in foster homes or "on own." There were also differences with respect to the type of placements used by the experimental and the nonexperimental programs. The nonexperimental programs more frequently returned patients to a parental home (39 per cent versus 24 per cent), while the experimental programs more frequently placed patients "on their own" (30 per cent versus 17 per cent) or in foster homes (13 per cent versus 6 per cent).

Several criteria for judging the rehabilitation outcome of the programs were used in this study, and are summarized in Table 17. Had only one criterion of rehabilitation success been used, for example, the foster home placement would have been judged as successful as most other types of placement from the standpoint of the criterion of SR-1 year. If rehabilitation is regarded as a two-stage process (i.e., not only success in remaining out of the hospital but also subsequent adjustment in the community), then the foster home placement was found to be the least successful of all types of placements.

The use of multiple criteria in judging the success of rehabilitation also permits evaluation of the manner in which various groups of patients were affected by the experimental program. With regard to the acute schizophrenic groups, the experimental Group I patient was better adjusted than his nonexperimental counterpart on two of the criteria, namely, his level of behavioral adjustment and his level of work adjustment at the 12th post-hospital month (see Table 17). The experimental Group II patient reached a significantly higher level of rehabilitation than his nonexperimental counterpart on two criteria: the level of hospital behavioral adjustment, and the number working full time after 12 months out of the hospital. In addition, the length of project hospitalization was shorter and the frequency of release was higher for the experimental than for the nonexperimental Group II patient, although this difference failed to reach the .05 level of significance. The experimental Group III patient reached a significantly higher level of rehabilitation on all in-hospital, one year follow-up, and six year follow-up criteria than his nonexperimental counterpart (see Table 17). With respect to the total group of 119 experimental and 208 nonexperimental patients, the experimental program had a significantly greater impact than the non-experimental program on six of the seven outcome criteria, but failed to reach the .05 level of significance for the six year follow-up of release-status differences. As noted earlier, however, this six year follow-up survey revealed a highly significant difference between the experimental and nonexperimental Group III patients.

One of the unique aspects of this research project was the non-selectivity of the schizophrenic sample studied and the avoidance of at-trition that would have decreased the size of the original groups of patients included in the project. Thus it is possible not only to judge the overall effectiveness of the rehabilitation approach used in the ex-perimental program for a wide range of schizophrenic patients in gen-eral, but also to determine the manner in which various kinds of patients were affected by the approach. Although the more chronically hos-pitalized patient group profited most by the approach used in the experimental program, the acute group of patients also responded sig-nificantly if one regards the criterion of out-for-a-year-and-working-full-time as important. Thus the enhancement and utilization of the psychi-atric aides' skills must be regarded as representing a significant step forward in the problem of the rehabilitation of hospitalized male schizo-phrenic patients.

The differences in rehabilitation between the patients of the two programs clearly suggest that the approach used in the experimental program was superior to the approach used in the nonexperimental programs. As discussed earlier, it is impossible to determine which of the experimental program's features resulted in these outcome differences. The wards of the Experimental Building were small and were arranged in sequence from closed to discharge. A psychologist and activity nurse often accompanied the patients and aides to the ward activity settings. The experimental program aides not only interacted more with their patients than their nonexperimental counterparts; they also participated more actively in decision making regarding their patients. This writer has attempted to describe, as completely as possible, all of the dimensions and operations of the experimental program. It can be stated with some certainty that if these program operations were duplicated elsewhere, the results would be similar to those reported herein.

It is this writer's opinion that each of these program elements is necessary but not sufficient by itself to produce the rehabilitation outcomes of this study. Many of these program elements are also interdependent on one another. The active interest of a significant professional staff person, for example, was shown to be a necessary condition for a high level of sustained aide-patient interaction. Likewise, the active involvement of the aide in the decision-making process was found to be a necessary condition in sustaining aide-patient interaction. It is less clear what effect the use of three small wards had on the program outcome. This writer would guess that the influence of the three wards was helpful, but not essential to the success of the experimental program. Each reader, however, will have to determine for himself the plausibility of these assumptions.

Our project has shown clearly that the role of a nonprofessionally trained person can be modified extensively in a psychiatric rehabilitation setting. When this modification takes the form of actively involving the nonprofessional in all phases of patient rehabilitation, the treatment outcome for hospitalized male schizophrenics is highly significant. In the final analysis the results of the experimental program can be explained most easily by stating that when a treatment program uses the resources of a large number of its personnel in a meaningful way, the program will be successful. If, on the other hand, the significant roles are restricted to the professional staff, the results will be distinctly less successful.

9

The Development and Utilization of
Professionally Untrained Manpower
· · · · ·
Reflections and Emerging Concepts

The present study indicates that the status hierarchy in the mental hospital does not necessarily correspond with the hierarchy of rehabilitation effectiveness. Certainly the psychiatric aide, who ordinarily has the least status in the mental hospital, can contribute significantly to the rehabilitation of hospitalized schizophrenic patients. In traditional programs, where the professional staff maintains the presumed relationship between status and treatment role, the therapeutic potential of the psychiatric aide is not likely to be developed.

The manner in which a mental hospital or clinic uses its human resources depends, to a large extent, on what resources it has available. Abundantly staffed with professional personnel, many training and research centers can afford to operate under the assumption that professional training is a necessary prerequisite for treatment effectiveness. These well-staffed centers are not likely to introduce program innovations that utilize the resources of nonprofessional manpower. Reinforcement therapy, for example, was first introduced in an inadequately staffed hospital at Weyburn, Saskatchewan (Ayllon and Michael, 1951). Used in many hospitals today, this approach depends primarily on the utilization of nursing personnel. Another approach, gaining in popularity, is the level system in which the patients become the primary therapeutic agents (Fairweather, 1964). This innovation was introduced in the continued treatment section of the VA Hospital in Palo Alto, California, a setting in which large groups of patients were served by relatively few professionally trained staff. Such innovations as these, then, are often adopted by centers that choose not to remain custodial, but which cannot rely on favorable staff-patient ratios for the operation of their therapeutic programs.

The introduction of programs that depend on nonprofessional personnel requires a unique relationship between professional and nonprofessional staff. The role of the professional becomes one of developing and enhancing the skills of the nonprofessional, for it seems uncertain that the nonprofessional, by himself, can achieve a high level of treatment effectiveness. It is difficult for most aides to develop a meaningful program structure, or to translate into operation such concepts as feedback to the patient, or expectancy for change. By assuming these responsibilities the professional staff can create a situation in which the nonprofessional plays his most effective role. Unless the professional staff, however, is willing to relinquish status gratification in exchange for an open and honest sharing of responsibility with the professionally untrained, an effective hospital program is unlikely to develop. It is also assumed that the professional staff are able to introduce and put into operation such treatment concepts as feedback, meaningful structure, role expectation and behavior modification. Unfortunately this assumption is not always justified, for many traditionally trained professionals are poorly prepared to do this. Nevertheless, in utilizing professionally untrained personnel, this is the role that the professional must play.

This chapter, then, attempts to highlight some of the processes and concepts in utilizing professionally untrained personnel. There arise out of our experiences with the psychiatric aide in the Fort Meade Hospital. Many of these concepts should be applicable to a wide range of settings engaged in utilizing nonprofessional manpower, such as programs in poverty, corrections, community mental health, and so on.

MEANINGFULLY INVOLVING NONPROFESSIONAL MANPOWER

In order for a program to function well, an important requirement is that its program personnel become interested and involved in their work. All too often, mental health programs are staffed with personnel who have become disinterested and uninvolved. This attitude, of course, is characteristic of the nontherapeutic person as reviewed in Chapter 2. At the very least, then, an effective program would seem to be one that promotes a high level of enthusiasm and involvement among its personnel.

In our study we were unusually successful in developing a high level of interest among our psychiatric aides. First of all, it was apparent to all of us that the aides really enjoyed working in the program. Within a short time after its beginning, the aides' wives, as already mentioned, began reporting that their husbands came home and talked about what they did and that, often for the first time, they took pride in and enjoyed their work. About a year after our program had started, a new modern building was opened and a call was sent out for staff. Our Experimental Building was the only one in which there was not a single aide who requested reassignment. A second source of evidence suggestive of a high level of satisfaction among our aides was the feeling of pleasure I experienced when I went to any of our three wards. There developed a great deal of observable spontaneity and warmth in the relationship between aides and patients. Our locked ward was one of the few locked wards I have ever enjoyed visiting. One sensed and observed in the actions of the aides a real respect for the dignity of the patient and a genuine warmth in the relationship. This is not to say that negative feelings were never expressed. Our aides felt free to tell a patient exactly what they thought of his behavior. Perhaps it was because of this freedom to express their feelings, both positive and negative, that there rarely seemed to be any "charged tension" in the air on any of our wards.

How did the aides' enthusiasm for and satisfaction with their work come about? These characteristics were not there to begin with, and we made no attempt to select aides who had these attributes initially. As suggested in the preceding paragraph, it was certainly related, in part, to the openness of communication between aides and patients. In addition, this openness also developed in their relationships with the activity therapists, activity nurse, research psychologist, and ward psychiatrist. It first occurred in a team meeting when an aide said to me, "Bob, I think that idea of yours is all wet." My immediate reaction was one of surprise, until I realized that this was precisely what I had been telling the aides; to say and do what they really felt like saying and doing. I had meant it as a guideline for their relationship to patients, and they had fortunately interpreted it much more broadly. I quickly recovered from the challenge, and listened while the aide told me why he felt as he did about my idea. After that, it became easier for the other aides to do the same and easier for me to accept and encourage this type of direct confrontation. In this way, the aides developed a freedom of expression that they rarely experience in most situations.

Another important factor that led to the aides' satisfaction and involvement with the program was my own conviction that they were a potentially untapped resource in the rehabilitation of the patient. Not only was I basically committed to this belief, but I was strongly motivated to devote my time and energy to developing and enhancing an aide-patient relationship characterized by openness, spontaniety, and genuineness. I discovered, however, that initially my feeling that the aide was potentially an interaction therapist par excellence was an expression of hope rather than of certainty. My own assumptions regarding the implied relationship between professional training and therapeutic effectiveness had not been completely clarified.

For example, I kept telling the aides that they had one basic guideline in relating to patients: to do and say what they really felt like saying and doing. During the first month, an aide lost his temper and kicked a resistive patient in the seat of the pants. I winced inside; it was the nurse who said to the aide, "I felt the same way." I nodded assent, for what she communicated so appropriately was: "It's OK to feel that way, but I neither support nor reject your action." This particular aide had tested us, and fortunately had not found a complete lack of support in our reaction to his acting as we had told him to. As the program progressed, he began to develop skill in expressing verbally those feelings that he initially kept to himself or expressed behaviorally. Because the aides found that we meant what we said with respect to their relating to patients, they became more open and spontaneous in their interaction with them. I found myself developing an increasing respect for the quality and effectiveness of these interactions.

Another belief which grew during the period of the study was that the aide, because of his intimate contact with, and knowledge about, patients, was an excellent decision maker and problem solver. For example, one patient eloped from the closed ward three times in a single week. He was very clever in hiding behind pillars while his escorted group went past, and then in escaping from the grounds. In the subsequent team meeting we held on his ward, two aides suggested that what he needed was a real boost to his self-confidence. Sensing that this patient felt very low, they suggested that he be transferred to an open ward to show him that we expected more of him. They felt he would live up to these expectations. The ward physician had already been informed by the hospital administration that they were tired of sending a car out after this man (three times in one week) and that we should "watch him." This I knew, but both the physician and I said "OK, let's give it a try"; underneath we wondered, "My God, what next?" The plan worked! Had we not risked it, we would have lost an accurate diagnosis of the situation and an excellent solution to the problem. It would have been easy to impose a solution of our own, but this would not have been the aides' solution. A solution that comes from the aides has the distinct advantage of being one to which they are committed, and, in my opinion, its potential for succeeding is thereby greatly enhanced.

Many other experiences like these proved to be opportunities whereby my statement of faith that aides were an untapped and traditionally ignored resource developed into a day-to-day operational philosophy. An aide would begin to say something about what he felt should be done. Sometimes he stated it so poorly that I tended to reject the content of what he was saying even before he had finished. I learned to listen, however, and I began to discover that what an aide might express poorly was yet often astute. Professional staff are often unable to communicate with or understand the aide; the gap in communication skill between them is great. One must learn to listen well.

I also learned that the aide's communication skills in talking with the patient were generally better than mine. Patients would tell aides things they never discussed with any of the professional staff. In retrospect, this should not have been too surprising, since many of our aides and patients had similar backgrounds and experiences; they talked the same language and shared similar values. As the program developed, I learned much from the aides about how to communicate with patients, how to pace myself in responding to the distrustful or slow-thinking patient, how to be direct at times when the situation required it.

A third important factor affecting the nonprofessional's level of involvement is the manner in which the professional staff present, and put into action, their treatment philosophy. Essentially, we had proposed to the aides that interaction pays off, that patients get better when one becomes open, genuine, and direct with them. Within the first two weeks, I risked putting this concept to the test, and I discovered that I had not been entirely convinced of its validity.

What happened was this: I became directly involved in the world of the aide and patient by spending most of my time in going to activities with patients from each of our wards. One patient in particular interested me. He sat at his loom quietly weaving his rug and hallucinating. I told the aides that I would bet them that if we all interacted with this patient, shared his activity with him, and confronted him with his behavior, his hallucinating would stop. This was the first real test of the concept that I wanted the aides to believe in, namely, that open and honest interaction pays off. I confess that I had certain apprehensions about testing the validity of this concept. Nevertheless, I took the risk and we tried it. Fortunately it worked, and within a few days the patient began to decrease his hallucinatory behavior and began to respond to us, talk with us, and trust us. This was the first real success of the program, and it went a long way in demonstrating to the aides, and to me as well, that the ability to modify behavior is not some magical quality possessed only by the professionally trained therapist. Not that the aides believed it was, but neither did they necessarily believe in their own potential skill in bringing about significant changes in patients' behavior and attitudes.

A basic ingredient in all effective therapeutic programs would seem to be that of personnel enthusiasm and involvement in their work. From our experience it seems clear that the professionally untrained person can indeed become highly committed to a rehabilitation program. In the present study, this commitment was enhanced by the openness of both aide-patient and aide-staff communication. If a nonprofessionally trained person feels that other staff don't listen to him, or that they regard his ideas as unimportant, he can hardly feel enthusiastic about what he is doing. Also, if communication between him and the staff is closed, the aide is likely to pattern his communication with patients in much the same way.

A second ingredient in developing the nonprofessionals' commitment to a program is that the staff, in turn, must believe that the nonprofessional is basically able to play an important therapeutic role. Even in this study, my own belief that the aide could effectively play the role of rehabilitation therapist was initially a statement of hope rather than conviction. As already pointed out, I discovered that the aides exceeded my expectations, and in my relationship with them I often found myself the learner rather than the teacher. It is not expected that a professionally trained person will find it easy to believe that a nonprofessional is as skilled as, or even more skilled than, he in many phases of patient rehabilitation. What is hoped, however, is that the professional can remain open to this possibility. Without at least this, it is likely that the nonprofessional will quickly discover what the other's role expectation of him is, and that he will perform at a level commensurate with such low expectation.

And finally, it has been suggested that the leader practice whatever rehabilitation philosophy he hopes the professionally untrained personnel will adopt. It is relatively easy to verbally endorse a treatment concept, but more difficult to personally test its validity in the public arena. Too many professional staff, in this writer's opinion, feel most comfortable in their offices, and are reluctant to become immersed in the world of the nonprofessional and the patient. Under these conditions, there can be little breaking down of the status and communication barriers which typically characterize the professional-nonprofessional relationship.

ENHANCING THE NONPROFESSIONAL'S EFFECTIVENESS

In this particular rehabilitation program, the role of the professional was that of bringing about changes in aide-patient relationship which enhanced the aides' therapeutic impact. Aside from encouraging the aide to become genuine and open in his relationship with patients, other program ingredients were introduced. First of all, there was the clearly communicated expectation of change in patient behavior. It became apparent to me that initially the aides believed that change was not likely to occur, especially in the chronic patient. These patients had been in the hospital a long time and, although they were new to me, to the aides their behavior represented an all-too-familiar pattern. I began to see differences in patients' behavior from day to day, and commented on these differences to the aides. I found myself developing a language of change in talking to the aides, asking them such questions as, "Do you see what's different in John today?" Through increased interaction with patients, change was indeed occurring and it became believable for us to expect and anticipate change. Had we not had these early successes in modifying patients' behavior, the program would undoubtedly not have had the success that it did.

Second, I offered a simple organizational structure or framework within which the aide could work effectively. We arranged our three wards in a progressive flow system. Patients were to move from the closed ward, to the open ward, to the discharge ward (the latter ward developed from an aide's suggestion). The basis for movement through this system was the behavioral adjustment of the patient, his taking part in the activity program at each ward level, and his assuming the responsibilities and privileges expected of him. It was the aides' job to help the patient modify his behavior to meet the expectancies of each ward and prepare for the next ward. The patient knew exactly where he stood, and the aide could tell the patient what he must do to move forward to the next ward. It seems to me that a simple and publicly adhered-to structure not only relieves the professional staff of involvement in routine decision making, but also enhances the problem solving of the nonprofessional since the latter knows just how much and what kinds of responsibilities he can assume in relating to his patient. Within a well-structured framework, he can help the patient much more than in traditional programs where he is only able to tell the patient, "That's up to the doctor. I don't know."

This orientation toward a framework of behavior modification made it unnecessary to pattern the aides' role after that of the professional. At one point we attempted to introduce group sessions in which each aide led his own therapy group. These meetings were awkward for both patients and aides because they were unaccustomed to talking in such a setting. Aides found it more productive to talk with the patient about what he did and felt, as they worked with him in the activity and recreational areas. In retrospect, I doubt that the inclusion of group therapy sessions would have added anything to the effectiveness of the program. Formal talk therapy is largely a social-class-related value, and is often perceived negatively by lower socioeconomic groups. When interest is taken in developing the aides' role, however, the professional too often attempts to make "junior professionals" out of untrained people, rather than enhancing the talents these people already have. In our program, I think that most of the aides and patients felt that task-oriented interaction had more to offer.

A third important characteristic of the program was the manner in which we increased the legitimacy of the nonprofessionals' role status, and thereby enhanced his involvement in effective problem-solving interaction. As noted in Chapter 5, we initially held the ward meetings in private, away from the patients. We wasted much time because the discussions would drift off to unrelated problems. Also in these private meetings, the professional staff dominated the discussion while the aides played a secondary role. Finally, I suggested that the meetings be held in the patients' dayroom, anticipating that much of our aimless discussion would stop. I was convinced that the aides knew what problems needed attention, which patients were adjusting well, and which patients were ready to move to a new ward. I felt that the aides should prepare the agenda for the meeting and should take responsibility for conducting it. This was done within a few months after the program started.

This change, in my opinion, achieved two things. First, the aide became an active participant in the problem-solving discussion about the ward. Second, the patient began to see that what the aide said not only was listened to by the staff, but was also acted upon. In essence, the significance of the aide increased in the patients' eyes, enhancing the meaningfulness of the interaction between them and the aide. At first, some patients tried to see the doctor in private to get him to make decisions regarding them. Initially, they were successful in this maneuver, but after the doctor was confronted with what he was doing, he sent the patients back to "work it out" with the aides. If the status of the nonprofessional is undercut in the patients' eyes, this renders him less effective in his relationship to those patients. Any professional, then, who hopes to enhance the rehabilitation effectiveness of untrained personnel should be very much concerned with the issues of increased status and commensurate responsibility. Otherwise, ideas and actions of the non-professional have no legitimacy in the patients' eyes.

In brief, the effectiveness of the nonprofessional can be enhanced. It is important that the nonprofessional be encouraged to look for and to respond to patient change. The program in which the nonprofessional works should be so structured that it is clear and readily understood. It should be a program that enhances the skills and is consonant with the values that the nonprofessional has already acquired through his own experiences in living. As discussed at the end of Chapter 5, formalized training was neither necessary nor desirable, for it would have substituted an alien set of values and skills. Recall, also, from Chapter 1 that the terms "professionally untrained" or "nonprofessional" do not necessarily imply lack of experience with respect to interpersonal-relationship skills or problems in living. Most of our aides were highly skilled in these areas, being married, raising children, assuming the responsibilities of providing for their families, and working with patients in a mental hospital setting. These nonprofessionals can become important and valued members of the rehabilitation team, however, *only if the professional regards them as such.* If, on the other hand, nonprofessionals are not given this status, both in words and actions, the patient will profit little from interaction with them.

In the final analysis, the catalyst that brings these program ingredients into play and largely determines a program's success is the quality of professional *leadership.* The presence of such ingredients as open communication and respect for the nonprofessional does not automatically insure a program's success. The most important ingredients of effective leadership include a deep commitment to a conceptualized plan of action, the ability to translate one's commitment and concepts into action, and the ability to communicate clearly with, and listen carefully to, one's staff. This is not to say that any program having a skilled leader will succeed, for I have seen a program fail badly that had an excellent leader but was built on questionable concepts. No program is so inherently good, on the other hand, that it will succeed under any and all circumstances. I have seen programs fail that were built on concepts that were basically valid, but that failed because there was no deep commitment on the part of the leader. He might verbalize the concepts well, but when a real test came he would behave by violating his verbally endorsed concepts. The importance of this leadership quality is well illustrated by the usual decrease in program effectiveness when a leader leaves and no other leadership emerges to fill the gap. It also explains, in my opinion, the fact that the originators of programs often obtain a degree of success that is not always experienced by others who attempt to replicate a reportedly successful program.

ROLE TRADITION
AND PROGRAM INNOVATION

The stimulus for program innovation ordinarily comes from those with moderate status in the organization. Those at the top resist change the most, while those at the bottom desire change but are in a relatively poor position to bring it about (Halpert, 1966). Continually thwarted, the less privileged reach a point where they not only lose a desire for change but actively resist any effort toward change. They fear that any innovation affecting them is most likely to be a change for the worse because no change that they favored had ever been put into effect (ibid., p. 235). The introduction of new programs, then, is difficult at best.

Once introduced, however, new programs rarely continue over a long period of time. Ideally, program innovation that results in increased treatment effectiveness should be accepted by an institution and become part of the operational procedure. In actuality, however, this seldom happens. Typically, once a project is over and the investigator leaves, staff roles modified during the project again become compatible with what was traditional for that institution. Such is partly the case with the aide-role project at Fort Meade. The professional staff now rarely attend activities with aides and patients, thereby serving as models for interaction. The high level of off-ward aide-patient interaction is no longer observed. Some residuals of the program remain: Team meetings continue to be held in the patients' dayroom. Also, the aides' status in that hospital is reportedly higher today than it was before the project was introduced. New aides, for example, hear the older aides describe the importance of their role in patient rehabilitation. Nevertheless, many of the program's operational characteristics have been modified or abandoned.

It may seem strange that a program with demonstrated effectiveness is later modified or abandoned by hospital staff. As discussed earlier, effective program innovation is very much a function of professional leadership. The aides' role is interdependent on the roles of the nurse, activity therapist, psychiatrist, and others. Unless the role changes introduced by program innovation are highly satisfying to those staff, innovation will not become part of the hospital operation once the "project" is over.

We were not particularly successful in developing among most of the professional staff a high level of satisfaction with, and commitment to, the program. The psychiatrist, who worked very well within the program structure, expressed this when he said, "I don't feel that a psychiatrist is really needed here." The social worker opposed many of the program's features, and finally maintained only a superficial contact with it. The chief of psychiatric service appeared to tolerate but not to endorse the program. The hospital director, whose own values were very much in keeping with the program's philosophy, nevertheless had to deal with some complaints from hospital personnel about it.

Had the openness of communication that our aides experienced occurred also with these key professional staff, changes could have taken place in their perception of the program and in their relationship with the aides. As it was, however, the program was looked upon as "the aides' program" or "Ellsworth's project." Most of the professional staff never came to believe that the aide was potentially a highly effective rehabilitation person. It is clear that I, too, at first did not quite believe this. Unlike the professional staff, however, I had the kind of relationship with the aides that permitted me to modify my initial reservations. The majority of professional staff did not, and I am sure they continued to underestimate the aides' potential. Thus a modification of their role in relationship to the aide was not regarded by them as necessary.

The role of the research psychologist was difficult for many to accept. During the first several months, I served as an active participant in the program itself and also as the coordinator of data collection. My role of participant in the team meetings and off-ward activities at times confused those who felt I should in no way personally influence the outcome of the program itself. Some felt strongly that the research hypothesis should be stated and that the psychologist should then collect and analyze data. Although such a position may have been appealing from an experimental point of view, it was obvious that in this way the research hypothesis would never have been translated into action. If an ongoing program using the aide as an active participant was to be implemented at all, the research psychologist had to support and assist in its development.

The team situation in which the aide played an active part has already been described. Its development, however, did not come about easily, and would not have occurred at all unless someone had taken a special interest in facilitating it. At first, I made a point of encouraging everyone to state his feelings and opinions honestly and openly. At times, a nonverbal gesture of an aide in response to a recommendation had to be picked up; "You don't look as if you agree with what Paul said, Joe. How do you feel?" At other times I was already aware that some one had privately expressed strong feelings about the way a patient was being handled, but was unwilling to share his feelings with the group. Under these circumstances, I would state the dissenting view as my own in order to support the expression of divergent viewpoints. It was two months before an aide said to me in a team meeting, "I don't agree with you." This was the turning point for the aide group, who then began to disagree openly with other members of the ward team, including the psychiatrist. These meetings then became much more spontaneous and lively with both patients and staff free to say what they really felt.

When the support for a modified role was withdrawn, the aide reverted to a more traditional role in keeping with the hospital's norms. Could it have been otherwise? Perhaps. What would have been needed, at the very least, was the participation of the hospital staff in planning for the program's continuation under a new leader. Plans were worked out with nursing service to establish a position for a full-time activity nurse. Receiving little outside support for this, however, nursing service never fully developed this role. Also, no professional leadership emerged to insure that the aide-role project could continue. Thus the project never acquired operational status within the hospital and was regarded as an experimental-demonstration program.

A more difficult approach in continuing the program would have been to change the hospital milieu and role expectancies. The program might then have been less dependent on the availability of effective leadership and more able to continue on its own. Only one report, known to this writer, describes such an effort (Ishiyama et al., 1966). Here the authors attempted to change the social situation in which the aide worked. Steps were taken to clarify the mission of the hospital, and develop a therapeutic role for the aides. Initially the increased status of the aide resulted in the hospital staff feeling threatened and perceiving the aide as "power hungry." These problems were worked through, however, and the aides are reported to be functioning quite differently. Also, an official reward system for excellence and achievement was set up for aides. Such action requires leadership at the highest level in the organization, although it is probable that many staff continue a strong latent commitment to a very different set of values. If the administrator were to leave, it is likely that this institution would also revert back to its previous role norms.

One of the most interesting aspects of the Ishiyama et al., study (ibid.) was the creation of the official reward system for aide achievement and effectiveness. Recall from Chapter 4 that treatment effectiveness is but one, and often one of the least important, of many goals of the bureaucratically organized mental hospital. By creating an official reward system for achievement and effectiveness, the goal of rehabilitation assumes more legitimacy in the mental hospital. If treatment effectiveness of a ward team, for example, could be measured and rewarded, there is little doubt that hospital staff would become more concerned about developing effective programs and less concerned about status hierarchy, role traditionalism, and the like. This approach offers much promise for the mental hospital, and warrants serious exploration.

It may be that role innovation in the utilization of professionally untrained people will occur more easily outside the institutional setting. In some mental health community clinics, for example, patient treatment is less encumbered by tradition than in most mental hospitals. There, getting the rehabilitation job done becomes more important than preserving the traditions of status hierarchy and role function. Also, communication problems are less difficult and the possibility of modifying role relationships and staff values is greater than it is in the large institution. This is not to say that role changes and innovations do not take place in the large institution. At the present time, however, they are highly dependent on the quality of leadership. Also, change takes place slowly. What was yesterday's innovation in a hospital setting becomes tomorrow's standard procedure. In other rehabilitation settings, yesterday's innovations may become today's procedures.

References

Ackner, B., Harris, A., and Oldham, A. J. Insulin treatment of schizophrenia: a controlled study. Lancet, 272:607–611, 1957
———— and Oldham, A. J. Insulin treatment of schizophrenia: a three year follow-up of a control study. Lancet, 281:504–506, 1962.
Anker, J. M., and Walsh, R. P. Group psychotherapy, a special activity program and group structure in the treatment of chronic schizophrenics. J. Consult. Psychol., 25:476–481, 1961.
Appleby, L. Intrusion: a social psychological approach to the treatment of chronic mental patients. Paper read before the meeting of the Kansas Occupational Therapy Association. Osawatomie State Hospital, Osawatomie, Kansas. March, 1958
———— Evaluation of treatment methods for chronic schizophrenia. Arch. Gen. Psychiat., 8:8–21, 1963.
Artiss, K. L. Milieu therapy in schizophrenia. New York, Grune & Stratton, 1962.
Ayllon, T., and Michael, J. The psychiatric nurse as a behavioral engineer. J. Exp. Anal. Behav., 2:323–334, 1951.
Bandura, A., and Walters, R. H. Social learning and Personality Development. New York, Holt, Rinehart, and Winston, 1963.
Bartemeier, L. H. Therapeutic results in mental hospitals with a minimum of professional personnel. Amer. J. Psychiat., 113:515–518, 1956.
Bateson, G. Schizophrenic distortions of communication. In Psychotherapy of Schizophrenic Patients, Whitaker, A., ed. Boston, Little, Brown and Co., 1958, Ch. 2.
Beck, J. C., Kantor, D., and Gelinean, V. A. Follow-up study of chronic psychotic patients "treated" by college case-aide volunteers. Amer. J. Psychiat., 120:269–271, 1963.
Becker, L. W. The process reactive distribution: a key to the problem of schizophrenia? J. Nerv. Ment. Dis., 129:442–449, 1959.
Belnap, I. Human Problems of a State Mental Hospital. New York, McGraw-Hill, 1956.
Berger, D. G., Rice, C. E., Sewall, L. G., and Lemkau, P. V. Post hospital evaluation of psychiatric patients: the social adjustment inventory method. Psychiatric Studies and Projects, 2:[No. 15], Dec., 1964.
Bergin, A. E. Some implications of psychotherapy research for therapeutic practice. J. Abnorm. Psychol., 71:235–246, 1966.

Bockoven, J. S. Moral treatment in American psychiatry. J. Nerv. Ment. Dis., 124:167–194, 292–321, 1956.

——— Some relationships between cultural attitudes toward individuality and care of the mentally ill. An historical study. In The Patient and the Mental Hospital, Greenblatt, M., Levinson, D., and Williams, R. H., eds. Glencoe, Ill., The Free Press, 1957, pp. 517–526.

Boyd, R., Baker, T., and Greenblatt, M. Ward social behavior: an analysis of patient interactions at highest and lowest levels. Nurs. Res., 3:77–79, 1954.

Bravos, T. A. Psychiatric administration, a challenge in organization. Mental Hospitals, 16:90–94, 1965.

Brill, H., and Patton, R. E. Analysis of population reduction in New York state mental hospitals during the first four years of large scale therapy with psychotropic drugs. Amer. J. Psychiat., 116:495–508, 1959

——— and Patton, R. E. Clinical-statistical analysis of population changes in New York state mental hospitals since introduction of psychotropic drugs. Presented at the American Psychiatric Association meeting, Chicago, May, 1961.

Brown, E. L., and Greenblatt, M. Social treatment. In From Custodial to Therapeutic Care in Mental Hospitals, Greenblatt, M., York, R. H., and Brown, E. L., eds. New York, Russell Sage Foundation, 1955, pp. 407–427.

Brown, G. W. Length of hospital stay and schizophrenia: a review of statistical studies. Acta Psychiat. Scand., 35:414–430, 1960.

Bryant, A. An investigation of processive-reactive schizophrenia with relation to perception of visual space. Unpublished doctoral dissertation. University of Utah, 1961.

Cameron, J. L., Laing, R. D., and McGhie, A. Patient and nurse: effects of environmental changes in the care of chronic schizophrenics. Lancet, 269:1384–1386, 1955.

Carkhuff, R. R., and Truax, C. B. The effects of lay group counseling, J. Consult. Psychol., 29:426–431, 1965.

Carson, R. C. A and B therapist "types"; a possible critical variable in psychotherapy. J. Nerv. Ment. Dis., 144:47–54, 1967.

Caudill, W. The Psychiatric Hospital as a Small Society. Cambridge, Mass., Harvard University Press, 1958.

——— Redlich, F. C., Gilmore, H. R., and Brody, E. B. Social structure and interaction processes on a psychiatric ward, Amer. J. Orthopsychiat., 22:314–334, 1952.

Chapman, L. J., Day, D., and Burnstein, A. The process-reactive distinction and prognosis in schizophrenia. J. Nerv. Ment. Dis., 133:383–391, 1961.

Colarelli, N. J., and Siegel, S. M. Ward H: An Adventure in Innovation. New York, D. Van Nostrand Co. Inc., 1966.

Cross, H. J. The outcome of psychotherapy: a selective analysis of research findings. J. Consult. Psychol., 28:413–417, 1964.

Cumming, E., Clancey, I. L. W., and Cumming, J. Improving patient care through organizational changes in the mental hospital. Psychiatry, 19:249–261, 1956.

Cumming, J., and Cumming, E. Social equilibrium and social change in the large mental hospital. In The Patient and the Mental Hospital, Greenblatt,

M., Levinson, D., and Williams, R. H., eds. Glencoe, Ill., The Free Press, 1957, Ch. 4, pp. 50–72.

Cutter, F., and Zappella, D. G. Mental health counselors: a bibliography Newsletter for Research in Psychology. V. A. Center. Hampton, Virginia. Feb., 1967

Deane, W. N. The reactions of a non-patient to a stay on a mental hospital ward. Psychiatry, 24:61–68, 1961.

Des Lauriers, A. Instruction and stimulation: the experience of reality in the psychotherapy of schizophrenia. Paper delivered at the 71st Annual American Psychological Association meeting, Philadelphia, 1963.

Dobson, W. R., and Ellsworth, R. B. Are hospital employees misinformed? Ment. Hosp., 11:36–39, Jan., 1960.

Donner, J. From the perspective of a mental health counselor. Newsletter. Division of Clinical Psychology, American Psychological Association, 18:9–12, 1965.

Downing, J. Chronic mental hospital dependency as a character defense. Psychiat. Q., 32 [No. 3]: 489–499, 1958.

Dreiblatt, I. S., and Weatherley, D. An evaluation of the efficacy of brief-contact therapy with hospitalized psychiatric patients. J. Consult. Psychol., 29:513–519, 1965.

Dunham, W. H., and Weinberg, S. The culture of the state mental hospital. Detroit, Wayne State University Press, 1960.

Ehrlich, D., and Sabshin, M. Psychiatrists' ideologies and psychotherapeutic functions for other helping professions. Paper presented at American Psychological Association meetings, Los Angeles, Sept. 4–9, 1964.

Ellsworth, R. B. The MACC behavioral adjustment scale; form I. Beverly Hills, Calif., Western Psychol. Serv., 1957.

———— The MACC behavioral adjustment scale; form II. Beverly Hills, Calif., Western Psychological Services, 1962 (revised form).

———— Bryant, A., and Butler, Grace. Psychiatric aide in-service training; an experimental approach. Nurs. Res., 9:12–16, Winter 1960.

———— and Clayton, W. H. Measurement of improvement in mental illness. J. Consult. Psychol., 23:15–20, 1959.

———— and Clayton, W. H. The effects of chemotherapy on length of stay and rate of return for psychiatrically hospitalized patients. J. Consult. Psychol., 24:50–53, 1960.

———— Mead, B. T., and Clayton, W. H. The rehabilitation and disposition of chronically hospitalized schizophrenic patients. Ment. Hyg., 22:343–348, July 1958

———— and Stokes, H. A. Staff attitudes and patient release. Psychiat. Studies and Projects, [No. 7], 1963.

Ewalds, R. M. Functions of the state mental hospital as a social institution. Ment. Hyg., 48:666–671, Oct. 1964.

Fairweather, G. W. Social Psychology in Treating Mental Illness: An Experimental Approach. New York, John Wiley and Sons, 1964.

———— and Simon, R. A further follow-up comparison of psychotherapeutic programs. J. Consult. Psychol., 27:76, 1963.

———— Simon, R., Gebhard, M. E., Weingarten, E., Holland, J. L., Sanders, R., Stone G. B., and Reahl J. E. Relative effectiveness of psychotherapeutic programs: a multicriteria comparison of four programs for three different patient groups. Psychol. Monogr., 74, [No. 5], 1960.

Federn, P. Ego Psychology and the Psychoses. New York, Basic Books, 1952.

Feldman, P. E. Inquiry into the use of psychotherapy for hospitalized schizophrenics. Amer. J. Psychiat., 118:405–409, 1961.

Ferguson, J. T., McReynolds, P., and Ballachey, E. L. Hospital Adjustment Scale, Stanford, California: Stanford University Press, 1953.

Forrer, G. R. An ego approach to psychotic behavior. Psychiat. Quart. Suppl., 2:1–8, 1958.

Frank, J. D. Persuasion and Healing, A Comparative Study. Baltimore, Johns Hopkins Press, 1961.

Freeman, H. E., and Simmons, O. G. The Mental Patient Comes Home. New York, John Wiley and Sons, 1963.

Freeman, T., Cameron, J. L., and McGhie, A. Chronic Schizophrenia. New York, International Universities Press Inc., 1958.

Galioni, E. F., Adams, F. H., and Tallman, F. F. Intensive treatment of back-ward patients, a controlled pilot study. Amer. J. Psychiat., 109:576–583, 1953.

Garfield, S. L., and Sundland, D. M. Prognostic scales in schizophrenia. J. Consult. Psychol., 30:18–24, 1966.

Garmezy, N., and Rodnick, E. N. Premorbid adjustment and performance in schizophrenia: implications for interpreting heterogeneity in schizophrenia. J. Nerv. Ment. Dis., 129:450–466, 1959.

Gilbert, D. C., and Levinson, D. J. Custodialism and humanism in mental hospital structure and in staff ideology. In The Patient and the Mental Hospital, Greenblatt, M., Levinson, D., and Williams, R. H., eds. Glencoe, Ill., The Free Press, 1957, pp. 20–35.

Glasser, W. Reality Therapy, a New Approach to Psychiatry. New York, Harper and Row, 1965.

Goode, W. J. Community within a community: the professions. Amer. Sociolog. Rev., 22:194–200, 1957.

Greenblatt M. The psychiatrist as social system clinician. In The Patient and the Mental Hospital, Greenblatt, M., Levinson, D., and Williams, R. H., eds. Glencoe, Ill., The Free Press, 1957.

———— Toward a therapeutic community. In From Custodial to Therapeutic Care in Mental Hospitals, Greenblatt, M., York, H., and Brown, E. L., eds. New York, Russell Sage Foundation, 1955, pp. 37–245.

Guilford, J. P. Fundamental Statistics in Psychology and Education. New York, McGraw-Hill, Inc., 1956.

Gurel, L. Correlates of psychiatric hospital effectiveness. Paper presented at 72nd Annual Convention of the American Psychological Association, Los Angeles, 1964.

———— Cohen, J., Davis, J. E., Stumpf, J. C., and Ullman, L. P. An assessment of psychiatric hospital effectiveness. Symposium presented at 72nd Annual Convention of the American Psychological Association, Los Angeles, 1964.

———— Release and community stay criteria in evaluating psychiatric treatment. In Psychopathology of Schizophrenia. New York, Grune & Stratton, 1966, Ch. 29.

———— Release and community stay in chronic schizophrenia. Am. J. Psychiat., 122:892–899, 1966a.

Gusick, J. L. Staff operations in a state mental hospital. Psychiatry, 20:309–312, 1957.

Gutenkauf, M., and Lundin, W. H. Emergent differences between two experimental ward cultures as a function of staffing ratio. Paper read at 66th Annual Meeting of the American Psychological Association, Washington, D.C., 1958.

Hall, B. H., Ganerni, M., Litt, M., Norris, V. L., Vail, U. H., and Sawatsky, G. Psychiatric Aide Education. New York, Grune & Stratton, 1952.

Halpert, H. P. Communications as a basic tool in promoting utilization of research findings. Community Ment. Health J., 2:231–236, 1966.

Higgins J. The Fort Meade aide-role project. Unpublished report sent to VA Hosp., Fort Meade, S. Dak., Nov., 1961.

Howard, B. F. Team work on an exit ward for the chronically ill. Ment. Hosp., 11:17–19, March, 1960.

Hyde, R. W., Bockoven, J., and York, R. H. Interaction of personnel and chronic psychotics. Final Report of National Institute of Mental Health Grant (unpublished). OM-99, June 1960.

———— and Williams, R. H. What is therapy and who does it? In The Patient and the Mental Hospital, Greenblatt, M., Levinson, D., and Williams, R. H., eds. Glencoe, Ill., The Free Press, 1957, Ch. 10, pp. 173–196.

Ishiyama, T., Grover, W. L., and Peterson, J. H. Milieu changes complement aide education. Hosp. Commu. Psychiat., 17:158–160, June, 1966.

Jacobsen, G. F. Crisis theory and treatment strategy: some social cultural and psychodynamic considerations. J. Nerv. Ment. Dis., 141:209–218, 1965.

Johnson, R., and McNeal, B. F. Residual psychopathology in released psychiatric patients and its relation to re-admission. J. Abn. Psychol., 70:337–342, 1965.

Johnson, W. People in Quandaries. New York, Harper and Bros., 1946.

Joint commission report on mental illness and health. Action for Mental Health. New York, Basic Books, 1961.

Jones, M. The concept of the therapeutic community. Amer. J. Psychiat., 112:647–650, 1956.

———— and Rapaport, R. The absorption of new doctors into a therapeutic community. In The Patient and the Mental Hospital, Greenblatt, M., Levinson, D., and Williams, R. H., eds. Glencoe, Ill., The Free Press, 1957, Ch. 14, pp. 248–262.

Kahne, M. J. Bureaucratic structure and impersonal experience in mental hospitals. Psychiatry, 22:363–375, 1959.

Kamman, G. R., Lucerno, R. J., Meyer, B. T., and Rechtschaffen, A. Critical evaluation of a total push program for regressed schizophrenics in a state hospital. Psychiat. Quart., 28:650–667, 1954.

Kantor, R. E., and Winder, C. L. The process-reactive continuum: a theoretical proposal. J. Nerv. Ment. Dis., 129:429–434, 1959.

Kellam, S. G. A method for assessing social contact: its application during a rehabilitation program on a psychiatric ward. J. Nerv. Ment. Dis., 132:-277–288, 1961.

Kennard, E. A. Psychiatry, administrative psychiatry, administration: a study of a veterans hospital. *In* The Patient and the Mental Hospital, Greenblatt, M., Levinson, D., and Williams, R. H., eds. Glencoe, Ill., The Free Press, 1957, Ch. 4, pp. 36–45.

Knupfer, G., Jackson, D. D., and Krieder, G. Personality differences between more and less competent psychotherapists as a function of criteria of competence. J. Nerv. Ment. Dis., 129:375–384, 1959.

Kramer, M., Goldstein, H., Israel, R. H., and Johnson, N. A. An historical study of the disposition of first admissions to a state mental hospital: experience of the Warren State Hospital during the period 1916–1950. Public Health Monogr., [No. 32]. Wash., D.C., U.S. Government Printing Office, 1955.

Lapolla, A. The intensive treatment of hospitalized mental patients. Paper read at 117th Annual Meeting of the American Psychiatric Association. Chicago, 1961.

Lasky, J., Haven, G., Smith, P., Bostion, D., Duffendack, S., and Nord, C. Post-hospital adjustment as predicted by psychiatric patients and by their staff. J. Consult. Psychol., 23:213–218, 1959.

Lawton, M. P. A study of psychiatric aides. Ment. Hosp., 15:512–515, Sept., 1964.

Levinson, D. J., and Gallagher, E. B. Patienthood in the Mental Hospital. Boston, Mass., Houghton, Mifflin Company, 1964.

—— and Sharof, M. R. Achieving a therapeutic ward setting. Ment. Hosp., 9:9–11, Sept., 1958.

Levy, R. A. Six-session outpatient therapy. Hosp. Community Psychiat., 17:340–343, Nov., 1966.

MacDonald, W. S. Small groups treatment of chronic mental patients: the problem of selectivity. Amer. J. Psychiat., 122:1298–1301, 1966.

Mainord, W. A., Burke, H. W., and Collins, L. G. Confrontation versus diversion in group treatment with chronic schizophrenics as measured by a positive incident criteria. J. Clin. Psychol., 21:222–225, 1965.

Marks, J., Stauffacher, J. C., and Lyle, C. Predicting outcome in schizophrenia. J. Abnorm. Soc. Psychol., 66:117–127, 1963.

McGregor, D. The Human Side of Enterprise. New York, McGraw-Hill, 1960.

McPartland, T. S., and Richart, R. H. Social and clinical outcomes of psychiatric treatment. Arch. Gen. Psychiat., 14:179–184, 1966.

Miller, D. Alternatives to mental patient rehospitalization. Commu. Ment. Health J., 2:124–128, 1966.

Miller, D. H. The rehabilitation of chronic open-ward neuropsychiatric patients. Psychiatry, 17:347–358, 1954.

—— and Clancy, J. An approach to the social rehabilitation of chronic psychotic patients. Psychiatry, 15:435–443, 1952.

Mishler, E. G. The nursing service and the aims of a psychiatric hospital: orientations of ward personnel to the care and rehabilitation of psychiatric patients. Amer. J. Psychiat., 111:664–672, 1955.

Morgan, T. H., and Gibson, M. Training of ward personnel. Ment. Hosp., 10:18, Feb., 1959.

—— and Hall, B. H. Report of an experiment in psychiatric aide training, Bull. Menninger Clin., 14:27–32, 1950.

Mouratides, N. Chronicity and decision making among professionals in mental hospitals. VA Cooperative Research Newsletter, 16–22, 1960.

Myerson, A. Theory and principles of the total push method in the treatment of chronic schizophrenia. Amer. J. Psychiat., 95:1197–1204, 1939.

Ozarin, Lucy D. Moral treatment and the mental hospital. Amer. J. Psychiat., 111:371–378, 1954.

Pace, R. E. Situational therapy. J. Personality, 25:578–588, 1957.

Paige, A. B., McMamara, H. J., and Fisch, R. I. A preliminary report on sensory stimulation therapy with chronic schizophrenics. Psychother. Theory of Research and Practice, 1: 133–136, 1964.

Paunez, A. Theory of the total push program in psychiatry. Amer. J. Psychother., 8:11–20, 1954.

Phillips, L. Case history data and prognosis in schizophrenia. J. Nerv. Ment. Dis., 117:515–525, 1953.

———— and Zigler, E. Role orientation (the action-thought dimension) and outcome in psychiatric disorder. J. Abnorm. Soc. Psychol., 68:381–389, 1954.

Pickford, E. M., and Taffel, C. Therapy and the psychiatrist. Psychiat. Quart., 32:335–341, 1958.

Pishkin, V., and Bradshaw, F. J. Prediction of response to trial visit in a neuropsychiatric population. J. Clin. Psychol., 16:85–88, 1960.

Pollack, E. S., Person, H., Kramer, M., and Goldstein, H. Patterns of retention, release, and death of first admissions to state mental hospitals. Public Health Monogr., [No. 58]. Washington, D.C., U.S. Government Printing Office, 1959.

Polonsky, N. A., White, R. B., and Miller, S. Determinants of the role-image of the patient in a psychiatric hospital. In The Patient and the Mental Hospital, Greenblatt, M., Levinson, D., and Williams, R. H., eds. Glencoe, Ill., The Free Press, 1957, Ch. 21, p. 386.

Poser, E. G. The effect of therapists' training on group therapeutic outcome. J. Consult. Psychol., 30:283–289, 1966.

Public Health Services Publication, No. 1151. Highlights from a survey of psychiatric aides. Wash., D.C., U.S. Department of Health, Education, and Welfare, 1964.

Reiff, R., and Riessman, F. The indigenous nonprofessional: a strategy of change in community action and community mental health programs. Nat. Inst. Labor Educ., Report No. 3, Nov., 1964.

Rioch, M. J. Changing concepts in the training of therapists. J. Consult. Psychol., 30:290–292, 1966.

———— Elkes, C., Flint, A. A., Vsdansky, B. S., Newman, R. G., and Silber, E. National Institute of Mental Health pilot study in training mental health counselors. Amer. J. Orthopsychiat., 33: 678–689, 1963.

Rogers, C. R. Some learnings from a study of psychotherapy with schizophrenics. Penn. Psychiat. Quart., 14:3–15, 1962.

Roos, P. Evaluation of psychotherapy as an adjunct to insulin coma therapy, J. Consult. Psychol., 25:450–455, 1961.

Sakel, M. New treatment of schizophrenia. Amer. J. Psychiat., 93:829–841, 1937.

Sanders, R. Personal communication. Denver, Colo., Dec., 1965.

———— Smith, R., Smith, A., Weinman, B., and Hunt, J. M. Social interaction therapy for the chronic psychotic: fact or fantasy. Symposium at 69th Annual Meeting of the American Psychological Association, New York, 1961.

Schofield, W. Psychotherapy: The Purchase of Friendship. New York, Prentice-Hall, 1964.

Schulberg, H. C. Future steps in implementing mental health plans. Commu. Ment. Health J., 2 (No. 2):157–162, Summer 1966.

Schwartz, M. S. What is therapeutic milieu? In The Patient and the Mental Hospital, Greenblatt, M., Levinson, D., and Williams, R. H., eds. Glencoe, Ill., The Free Press, 1957, pp. 130–137.

Shatin, L. Some psychological aspects of long term hospitalization. Ment. Hyg., 41:487–496, 1957.

Sheppard, M., Goodman, N., and Watt, D. C. The application of hospital statistics in the evaluation of pharmacotherapy in a psychiatric population, Compr. Psychiat., 2:11–19, 1961.

Sines, J. O., Lucero, R. J., and Kammon, G. R. A state hospital total push program for regressed schizophrenics. J. Clin. Psychol., 8:189–193, 1952.

Sines, L. K. Some dimensions of the therapeutic personality. Unpublished study, Fergus Falls State Hospital, Fergus Falls, Minn., 1959.

Spohn, H., Diethelm, O., Klebanoff, S., and Rackow, L. L. The efficacy of a socio-environmental program in the treatment of chronic schizophrenics. FDR Researcher. Publication of VA Hosp., Montrose, N.Y., 2:21–24, June, 1963.

Staudt, V. M., and Zubin, J. A biometric evaluation of the somato-therapies in schizophrenia. Psychol. Bull., 54:171–196, 1957.

Stevenson, I. The challenge of results in psychotherapy. J. Psychiat., 116:120–123, 1959.

Stotsky, B. A. A successful nursing home placement program. Hosp. and Commu. Psychiat., 17:337–339, Nov., 1966.

Straus, A. Psychiatric Ideologies and Institutions. New York, The Free Press, 1964.

Stringham, J. A. Rehabilitating chronic neuropsychiatric patients. Amer. J. Psychiat., 108:924–928, 1952.

Szasz, T. S. A contribution to the psychology of schizophrenia, Arch. Neur. Psychiat., 77:420–436, 1957.

Unterberger, H. Psychodynamics and rehabilitation. Ment. Hosp., 10:18–21, Dec., 1959.

Vaughn, R. Preliminary report on the model ward-personnel training project. Report submitted to the National Institute of Health, OM-331, Oct., 1961.

Vernallis, F., and Reinert, R. E. An evaluation of a goal directed group psychotherapy with hospitalized patients. Group Psychother., 14:5–12, 1961.

Vitale, J. H. The therapeutic community, a review article. In The Psychiatric Hospital as a Social System, Wessen, A. F., ed. Springfield, Ill., Charles C Thomas, Publisher, 1964, pp. 91–110.

Walker, R. G., and Kelley, F. E. Short term psychotherapy with hospitalized schizophrenic patients. Acta Psychiat. Scand., 35:34–56, 1960.

——— and Kelley, F. E. Short term psychotherapy with schizophrenic patients evaluated over a three-year follow-up period. J. Nerv. Ment. Dis., 137:349–352, 1963.

Weber, M. The Theory of Social and Economic Organization. Trans. by Henderson, A. M., and Parsons, T. Parsons, T., ed. New York, Oxford University Press, 1947.

Whitehorn, J. C., and Betz, B. J. A study of psychotherapeutic relationships between physicians and schizophrenic patients, Amer. J. Psychiat., 111:321–331, 1954.

——— and Betz, B. J. A comparison of psychotherapeutic relationships between physicians and schizophrenic patients when insulin is combined with psychotherapy and when psychotherapy is used alone. Amer. J. Psychiat., 113:901–910, 1957.

——— and Betz, B. J. Further studies of the doctor as a crucial variable in the outcome of treatments with schizophrenic patients. Amer. J. Psychiat., 117:215–223, 1960.

Wickland, R. A new approach to the treatment and rehabilitation of hospitalized chronic schizophrenics. Paper presented at 33rd Annual Meeting of the Western Psychological Association. Santa Monica, California, 1963.

Wittman, M. P. A scale for measuring prognosis in schizophrenic patients. Elgin State Hospital Papers, Ill., 4:20–33, 1941.

Witton, K., and Ellsworth, R. B. Social and psychological (MMPI) changes 5–10 years after lobotomy. Dis. Nerv. Syst., 23:1–4, 1962.

Yamamoto, J., and Goin, M. C. Social class factors relevant for psychiatric treatment, J. Nerv. Ment. Dis., 142:332–339, 1966.

York, R. H. Experiments in ward patient care at Bedford Veterans Administration Hospital. In From Custodial to Therapeutic Care in Mental Hospitals, Greenblatt, M., York, R. H., and Brown, E. L., eds. New York, Russell Sage Foundation, 1955, pp. 249–348.

Zinct, C. N., and Fine, H. J. Perceptual differentiation and two dimensions of schizophrenia. J. Nerv. Ment. Dis., 129:435–441, 1959.

Zolik, E. S., and Lantz, F. M. Patient return rates of two mental hospitals. Virginia Medical Monthly, pp. 139–142, March, 1965.

PART THREE

Appendices

appendix A

PERSONNEL-PATIENT INTERACTION
RATING SCALE

Employee's Name	Rater's Name	Date	Activity

This scale is designed to study the amount of interaction which takes place between patients and personnel (aides particularly) in an off-ward activity setting. The scale is to be used for research purposes only. Since this scale will be used for obtaining an "overall" picture of the personnel-patient interaction, the ratings on this scale will *not* be used as part of the employees' performance rating, nor will they come to the attention of the employees' supervisor. (Later changed for use in counseling.)

In question number 1, *circle* the number above the approximate amount of time the aide spends in actual *patient contact activities* (talking with and working with *patients*). Observing patients, talking with other personnel etc. are *not* patient contact activities and the amount of time the aide spends in these nonpatient contact activities will directly reduce the amount of time in patient contact activities.

The remaining items are to be used to describe the kind of interaction the aide has with patients. On items 2 to 8, circle the number above that behavior which most typically describes the aide's behavior. Circle one number for each question.

Be sure to rate the aide's behavior as you have observed him for that day. *DO NOT RATE ON THE BASIS OF YOUR OVERALL GENERAL IMPRESSION OF THE AIDE.*

----

1. HOW MUCH TIME DOES THE AIDE SPEND IN PATIENT-CONTACT ACTIVITY, TALKING WITH THEM AND/OR DOING THINGS WITH THEM?

2	3	4	5	6	7
Almost Never (About 10%)	Rarely (About 20%)	Sometimes (About 40%)	Frequently (About 60%)	Usually (About 80%)	Almost Always (About 90%)

2. HOW OFTEN DOES THE AIDE MAKE BRIEF COMMENTS TO THE PATIENT SUCH AS "NICE WORK, COME OVER HERE, STOP THAT, GO SIT DOWN,"

ETC. THESE COMMENTS ARISE FROM AN AIDE WHO IS ALERT AND AWARE
OF WHAT IS TAKING PLACE IN THE AREA, AND MAKES BRIEF COMMENTS
TO THE PATIENTS ABOUT THEIR BEHAVIOR.

1	2	3
Almost Never	Sometimes	Frequently

3. HOW OFTEN DOES THE AIDE ATTEMPT TO ENTER INTO A "GIVE-AND-
TAKE" CONVERSATION WITH A PATIENT WHO IS NOT PARTICULARLY
WITHDRAWN, TRYING TO TALK TO PATIENT AND GETTING THE PATIENT
TALKING TO HIM?

1	3	5
Almost Never	Sometimes	Frequently

4. HOW OFTEN DOES THE AIDE ATTEMPT TO INVOLVE A WITHDRAWN
PATIENT INTO CONVERSATION OR ACTIVITY WITH HIMSELF AND OTHERS?
GO OUT OF HIS WAY TO STIMULATE THE WITHDRAWN PATIENT TO BE-
COME A PART OF THE ACTIVITY?

1	4	7
Almost Never	Sometimes	Frequently

5. HOW OFTEN DOES THE AIDE TRY TO TALK WITH TWO OR MORE
PATIENTS, ATTEMPTING TO GET THEM INVOLVED IN CONVERSATION WITH
HIM AND EACH OTHER, ATTEMPTING TO GET THEM AWARE OF WHAT
THE OTHER IS DOING AND SAYING?

1	3	5
Almost Never	Sometimes	Frequently

6. HOW OFTEN DOES THE AIDE TAKE PART IN THE ACTIVITIES WITH THE
PATIENTS, TRYING TO BECOME A PART OF THEIR ACTIVITIES (GAMES,
MAKING THINGS, WORKING, ETC.) IN A HELPFUL MANNER? PARTICI-
PATING WITH THE PATIENTS IN THEIR ACTIVITIES?

1	3	5
Almost Never	Sometimes	Frequently

7. HOW OFTEN DOES THE AIDE ATTEMPT TO PROMOTE A GROUP ACTIVITY,
STIMULATING A GROUP OF PATIENTS TO TAKE PART IN A GROUP GAME,
OR PROJECT? IN GENERAL, ATTEMPTING TO STIMULATE A GROUP OF
NONACTIVE PATIENTS INTO A GROUP ACTIVITY, PATIENTS WHO WOULD
NOT HAVE BEEN ABLE TO START OR CONTINUE A GROUP ACTIVITY ON
THEIR OWN (NOT JUST PLAYING POOL WITH A GROUP OF ACTIVE,
INTERESTED PATIENTS)?

1	4	7
Almost Never	Sometimes	Frequently

8. DOES THE AIDE <u>INTERACT</u> WITH A WIDE VARIETY OF PATIENTS OR SPEND
HIS TIME WITH ONLY ONE OR TWO "FAVORITE" PATIENTS DURING THE
ACTIVITY PERIOD?

1	4	7
Only 1–2 different patients	Only 3–6 different patients	7 or more different patients

Score ___ + ___ + ___ + ___ + ___ + ___ + ___ + ___ = ___
　　　　1　　2　　3　　4　　5　　6　　7　　8　　Total

Percentile

Note: The differential scoring for each item reflects staff judgments regarding
that item's relative therapeutic value.

appendix B

TEAM MEETING QUESTIONNAIRE

_____

Code

1. Please fill in the space above (Code—Upper right hand corner) according to instructions.
2. Following are a number of statements concerning your feelings about Ward Team Meetings. Complete each statement by circling the word below it which describes your feelings.

   for example:

I AM ON TIME TO MY TEAM MEETINGS
Always   Usually   Sometimes   Rarely   Never

   If you are "Always" on time, you would circle Always. If you are "Rarely" on time, circle Rarely, and so on.

3. IMPORTANT: You are not asked to write your name on this questionnaire because we want you to be completely free to answer each question honestly. When you finish answering the questionnaire, you will fold it in half and drop it into a sealed box.

   If you feel that you cannot answer a question in terms of how you honestly feel, leave the question unanswered and go on to the next one. We would rather have a question left unanswered than have one which is incorrectly filled out.

   Thank you.

   Now go on to the next page.

1. IN OUR TEAM MEETINGS WE SPEND TOO MUCH TIME ACCOMPLISHING
   TOO LITTLE
   Always   Usually   Sometimes   Rarely   Never

2. I REALLY LOOK FORWARD TO ATTENDING OUR TEAM MEETINGS
   Always   Usually   Sometimes   Rarely   Never

3. IT IS IMPORTANT TO ME TO BE A MEMBER OF THE TEAM
   Very   Rather   Sometimes   Makes   Makes
   Important   Important   Important   Very Little   Absolutely
                                                       Difference   No Difference

4. I REALLY FEEL I PLAY AN IMPORTANT PART IN HELPING MAKE OUR
   TEAM DECISIONS
   Always   Usually   Sometimes   Rarely   Never

5. ACTUALLY, THE TEAM MEETINGS ARE JUST A WASTE OF MY TIME
   Always   Usually   Sometimes   Rarely   Never

6. THE DECISIONS OUR TEAM MAKES ARE THE DECISIONS THE DOCTORS
   (PHYSICIANS) HAD IN MIND IN THE FIRST PLACE
   Always   Usually   Sometimes   Rarely   Never

7. PEOPLE REALLY WANT TO KNOW WHAT I THINK AND WANT TO HEAR
   WHAT I HAVE TO SAY IN TEAM MEETINGS
   Always   Usually   Sometimes   Rarely   Never

8. THE REASON I GO TO TEAM MEETINGS IS ONLY BECAUSE SOMEBODY
   EXPECTS ME TO BE THERE
   Always   Usually   Sometimes   Rarely   Never

9. TEAM MEETINGS COULD BE IMPROVED A LOT
   Definitely   Probably   Don't Know   Probably   Definitely
   True   True   Untrue   Untrue

10. EVERYBODY ON OUR TEAM HAS AN EQUAL VOICE IN MAKING DECISIONS
    Always   Usually   Sometimes   Rarely   Never

11. WHEN IT COMES RIGHT DOWN TO IT, THE DOCTORS (PHYSICIANS)
    REALLY MAKE THE DECISIONS
    Always   Usually   Sometimes   Rarely   Never

12. WHEN I DON'T SAY ANYTHING IN TEAM, IT'S BECAUSE I FEEL I DON'T
    KNOW THE PATIENTS WELL ENOUGH
    Always   Usually   Sometimes   Rarely   Never

13. WHEN I DON'T SAY ANYTHING IN TEAM, IT'S BECAUSE I'M NOT REALLY
QUALIFIED
Always   Usually   Sometimes   Rarely   Never

14. WHEN I ATTEND A TEAM MEETING, I FEEL KIND OF "OWLY"
Always   Usually   Sometimes   Rarely   Never

15. IF I WERE TOLD I WAS BEING REPLACED BY SOMEBODY ELSE ON OUR
TEAM, I WOULD FEEL QUITE UPSET
Definitely   Probably   Don't Know   Probably   Definitely
  True   True   Untrue   Untrue

16. I FEEL AS THOUGH I'M AS IMPORTANT AS ANYBODY ELSE ON THE TEAM
Always   Usually   Sometimes   Rarely   Never

17. TEAM MEETINGS SHOULD BE DISCONTINUED
Definitely   Probably   Don't Know   Probably   Definitely
  True   True   Untrue   Untrue

18. WHEN I DO SAY SOMETHING IN TEAM, I GET THE IMPRESSION I'VE
"SPOKEN OUT OF TURN"
Always   Usually   Sometimes   Rarely   Never

19. PEOPLE IN TEAM SEEM REALLY INTERESTED IN WHAT'S GOING ON
Always   Usually   Sometimes   Rarely   Never

20. TEAM MEETINGS TEACH ME THINGS WHICH HELP ME DEAL WITH
PATIENTS IN GENERAL
Always   Usually   Sometimes   Rarely   Never

21. TEAM MEETINGS TEACH ME THINGS WHICH HELP ME TO DEAL MORE
EFFECTIVELY WITH THE PARTICULAR PATIENT BEING PRESENTED
Definitely   Probably   Don't Know   Probably   Definitely
  True   True   Untrue   Untrue

appendix C

VETERANS ADMINISTRATION HOSPITAL
Ft. Meade, South Dakota
(Adopted from Fairweather *et al.*, 1960)

183A

Date: _____

Please complete each of the nine statements by checking the phrase that best describes how the veteran is getting along as of this date. Check only one of each set of phrases. An example is given below:

Example: The veteran came to this hospital because he was a
_____Plumber.
_____Veteran who needed help.
_____Electrician.
_____Salesman.

The phrase to check is *veteran who needed help*. You will note a check opposite the term *veteran who needed help*. Now fill out the following nine items by checking the phrase which best tells how Mr._____ is getting along.

1. Right now the veteran is:
   a. _____Back in the hospital for nervousness.
   b. _____Under doctor's care for nervousness.
   c. _____Out of the hospital and getting treatment for nervousness.
   d. _____Out of the hospital, but has been in and out of a mental hospital since he left Ft. Meade. (explain below)
   e. _____Other, explain. _____

   _____

   _____

197

2. Since he left the hospital, the veteran has:
   a. _____Worked full-time.
   b. _____Worked half-time.
   c. _____Been unemployed.
   d. _____Other, explain. _____

   _____

   _____

3. Since he left the hospital, the veteran:
   a. _____Gets together with many friends regularly.
   b. _____Has had one or two friends.
   c. _____Has had no close friends or buddies.
   d. _____Likes to be alone most of the time.

4. The veteran:
   a. _____Often talks with the people he lives with.
   b. _____Sometimes talks with the people he lives with.
   c. _____Rarely talks with the people he lives with.
   d. _____Never talks to the people he lives with.

5. In my opinion, the veteran is:
   a. _____Getting along very well.
   b. _____Getting along fairly well.
   c. _____Getting along satisfactorily.
   d. _____Getting along poorly.

6. In my opinion, the veteran is:
   a. _____Easy to get along with.
   b. _____Occasionally hard to get along with.
   c. _____Usually hard to get along with.
   d. _____Extremely trying to get along with.

7. In my opinion, the veteran is:
   a. ————Well most of the time.
   b. ————Well some of the time.
   c. ————Not well most of the time.
   d. ————Very sick.

8. The veteran:
   a. _____Never drinks.
   b. _____Drinks once in a while.
   c. _____Drinks a lot but stays out of trouble.
   d. _____Heavy drinker and gets in trouble.

9. Since the veteran left the hospital:
   a. _____He has had no trouble with the law.
   b. _____He has been in trouble with the law.

                                                        Very truly yours,

Index